Complete
Canadian
Curriculum

MATH
ENGLISH
SOCIAL STUDIES
SCIENCE

Grade **1**

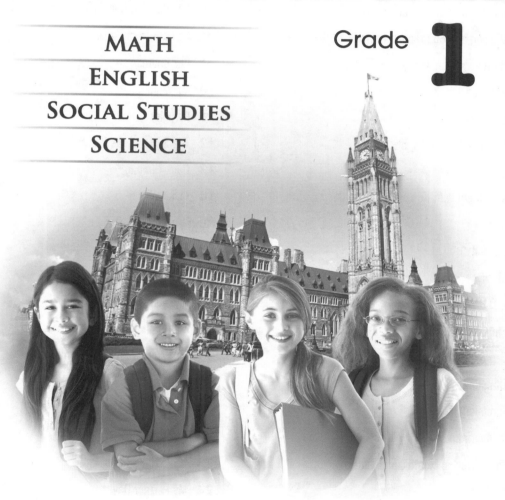

Printed in China

D1318534

ISBN: 978-1-897164-29-7

Contents　Grade 1

<table>
<tr><td colspan="3">Mathematics</td><td colspan="3">English</td></tr>
</table>

ISBN: 978-1-897164-29-7

Social Studies

Science

Answers

ISBN: 978-1-897164-29-7

ISBN: 978-1-897164-29-7

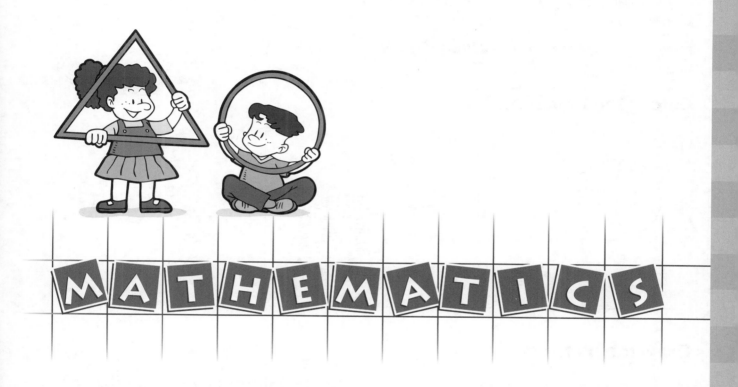

ISBN: 978-1-897164-29-7

1

Comparison

- Compare the sizes, heights, and lengths of different things.
- Use words such as "bigger", "biggest", "taller", and "tallest" to describe objects.

I'm the biggest.

I'm smaller than the dog.

Colour the bigger one.

①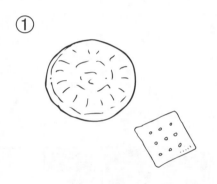

②

③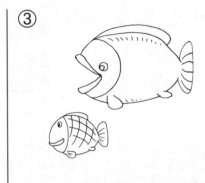

Draw the pictures.

④ a smaller house

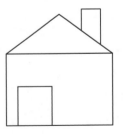

⑤ a bigger butterfly

⑥ a smaller cat

ISBN: 978-1-897164-29-7

Check ✔ the taller one.

⑦ Ⓐ Ⓑ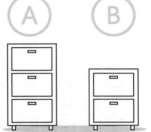

⑧  Ⓐ Ⓑ

⑨ Ⓐ Ⓑ

⑩ Ⓐ Ⓑ

⑪ Ⓐ Ⓑ

⑫ Ⓐ Ⓑ

Colour the longer one.

⑬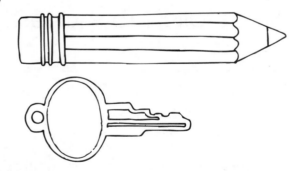

⑭

⑮

⑯

ISBN: 978-1-897164-29-7

Put each group of things in order. Write the letters.

⑰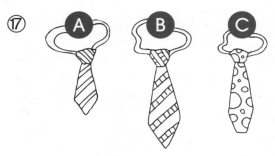

From longest to shortest:

_____

⑱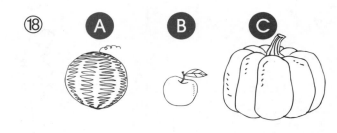

From smallest to biggest:

_____

⑲

From biggest to smallest:

_____

⑳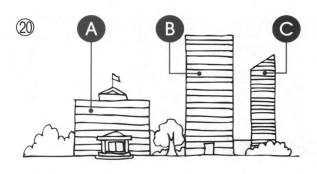

From tallest to shortest:

_____

㉑

From biggest to smallest:

_____

From tallest to shortest:

_____

ISBN: 978-1-897164-29-7

Draw one longer bracelet and one that has the same length as the one shown.

㉒

Look at the picture. Fill in the blanks with the correct words.

longer   longest
taller   tallest
shorter   shortest
same
smaller   smallest
bigger   biggest

㉓ Amy and Sue have the _____ height.

㉔ Tom's shoes are _____ than Amy's shoes.

㉕ Tom's shoes are the _____ .

㉖ Amy's hair is _____ than Mrs. Green's hair.

㉗ Tom's hair is _____ than Sue's hair.

㉘ The belt is _____ than the rope.

ISBN: 978-1-897164-29-7

More about Comparison

- Compare the width, thickness, and weight of different objects.
- Compare numbers of different groups of objects.

> *This is the widest that I can open my mouth.*

Colour the wider one in each pair.

①

②

③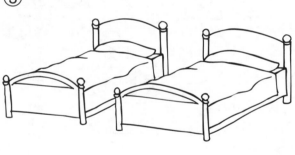

④

Complete the drawings.

⑤ a narrower door

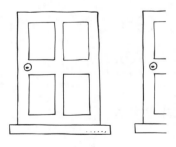

⑥ a narrower ladder

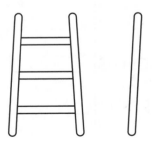

ISBN: 978-1-897164-29-7

Colour the thicker one.

⑦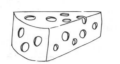

⑧

⑨

⑩

Complete the drawings.

⑪ a thicker sandwich

⑫ a thinner hamburger

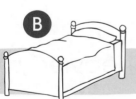

Look at the pictures. Fill in the blanks with letters.

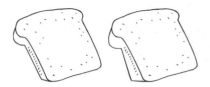

A   B   C

⑬ The thickest mattress: _____

⑭ The thinnest mattress: _____

⑮ *I want to jump on a bed. Which one is the best?*

_____

ISBN: 978-1-897164-29-7

2

Circle ◯ the heavier one in each pair.

⑯

⑰

⑱

⑲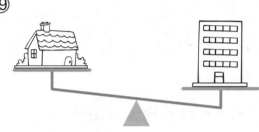

⑳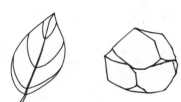

㉑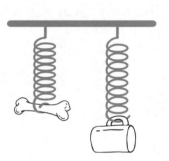

Look at the picture. Circle ◯ the correct words or picture.

㉒ is   heavier / lighter   than .

㉓ is   heavier / lighter   than .

㉔   is the heaviest.

ISBN: 978-1-897164-29-7

Circle ◯ the group with more items.

㉕

㉖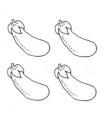

Colour the group with the most items.

㉗

㉘

Look at the pictures.   Answer the questions.

Ⓐ    Ⓑ    Ⓒ

㉙ Which pond has the most fish?   _____

㉚ Which pond has the fewest fish?   _____

㉛ Which pond has more fish than ?   _____

ISBN: 978-1-897164-29-7

3

Ordering and Sorting

My toys.

- Order things by their sizes, heights, numbers, etc.
- Sort things out with simple rules.
- Make rules to organize things.

Ben's toys

Check ✔ the group with objects put in order.

①  ⟶ ○

②  ⟶ ○

③ 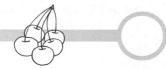 ⟶ ○

④  ⟶ ○

⑤ ⟶ ○

ISBN: 978-1-897164-29-7

Put the things in the correct order.   Write the letters.

⑥ Ⓐ 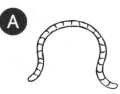 Ⓑ 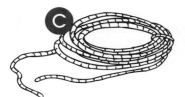 Ⓒ 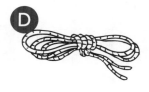 Ⓓ

From shortest to longest: ____ , ____ , ____ , ____

⑦ Ⓐ  Ⓑ Ⓒ   Ⓓ

From biggest to smallest: ____ , ____ , ____ , ____

⑧ Ⓐ Ⓑ Ⓒ Ⓓ

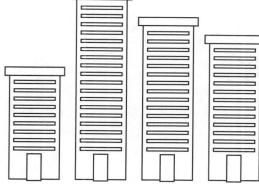

From tallest to shortest:

____ , ____ , ____ , ____

⑨

From fewest to most:

____ , ____ , ____ , ____

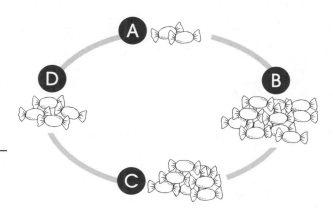

ISBN: 978-1-897164-29-7

Cross out ✗ the item that does not belong in each group.

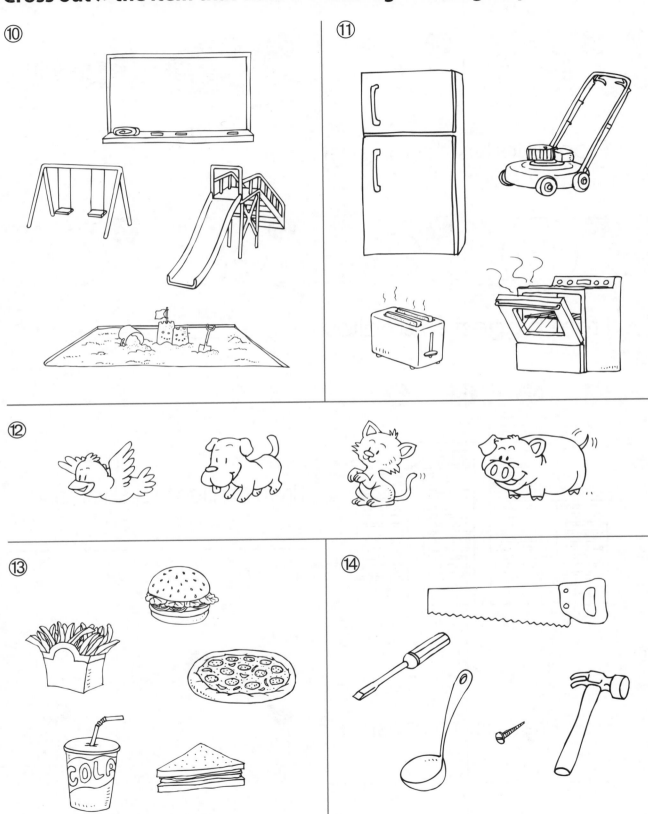

⑩

⑪

⑫

⑬

⑭

ISBN: 978-1-897164-29-7

When you write the rule to sort some items, look carefully to find the common characteristic of the items first. There may be more than one way to sort them.

e.g.

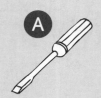

Tools: **A, C**

Utensils: **B, D**

Look at the items in each group. Write the sorting rule. Then sort the items.

⑮

☐ : _____

☐ : _____

⑯

☐ : _____

☐ : _____

ISBN: 978-1-897164-29-7

4

Sequencing

- Understand the sequence of some events in daily lives.
- Use ordinal numbers to describe the position of people or objects in a group.

Look at the pictures. Put them in the correct sequence. Write the letters.

①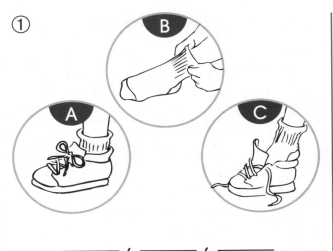

——— , ——— , ———

②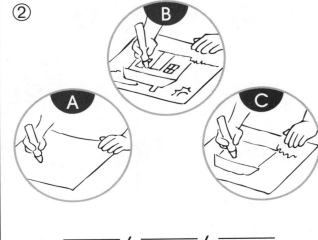

——— , ——— , ———

③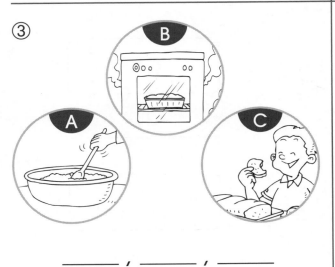

——— , ——— , ———

④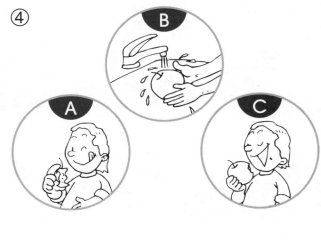

——— , ——— , ———

ISBN: 978-1-897164-29-7

Put the pictures in the correct sequence. Write the letters. Then colour the picture that comes next.

⑤

A   B   C   D

Sequence:

_____ , _____ , _____ , _____

⑥

A   B   C   D

Sequence:

_____ , _____ , _____ , _____

⑦

A   B   C   D

Sequence:

_____ , _____ , _____ , _____

ISBN: 978-1-897164-29-7

Look at each group of things. Colour the first one yellow, the third one blue, and the sixth one red. Then find the position.

⑧

This apple is the _____ .

⑨

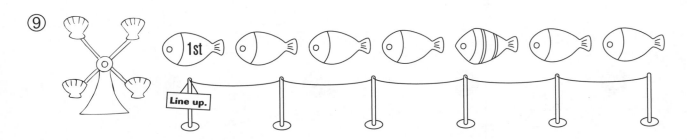

The position of 🐟 : _____

⑩

The position of 🎈 : _____

⑪ The position of ⚽ :

_____

ISBN: 978-1-897164-29-7

Ordinal numbers:

I like the 8th flower.

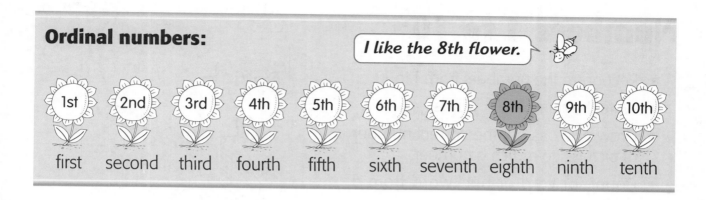

| 1st | 2nd | 3rd | 4th | 5th | 6th | 7th | 8th | 9th | 10th |
| first | second | third | fourth | fifth | sixth | seventh | eighth | ninth | tenth |

Write the ordinal numbers in words.

⑫ 5th _____

⑬ 7th _____

⑭ 2nd _____

⑮ 8th _____

⑯ 1st _____

⑰ 4th _____

Look at the pictures.   Write the correct ordinal numbers.

⑱

I'm the _____ and
you're the _____ .

⑲

You have a chain of food.
The _____ , _____ , and
_____ are sausages.

ISBN: 978-1-897164-29-7

Numbers 1 to 10

- Recognize the numbers from 1 to 10.
- Write the numbers in words.
- Draw or cross out the correct number of pictures to match a number.
- Count forward or backward from a given number.

5 gifts.

Count and write the numbers.

①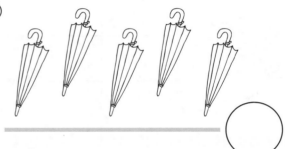

②

_____ ◯

_____ ◯

③

_____ ◯

④

_____ ◯

⑤

_____ ◯

⑥

_____ ◯

ISBN: 978-1-897164-29-7

Count and write the numbers in words.

⑦

_____ bees

⑧

_____ birds

⑨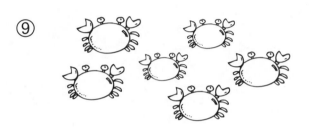

_____ crabs

⑩

_____ flowers

⑪

_____ frogs

⑫

_____ rings

Write the number that comes after.

⑬ 5 _____

⑭ 9 _____

⑮ 2 _____

Write the number that comes before.

⑯ _____ 9

⑰ _____ 4

⑱ _____ 7

ISBN: 978-1-897164-29-7

Draw 1 more item in each group. Then count and write the number.

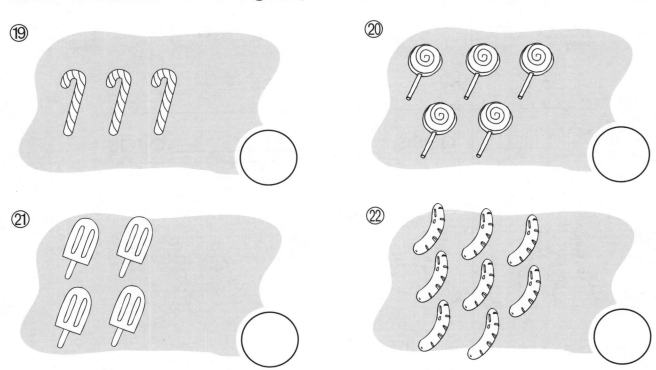

㉑ ㉒

Draw or cross out ✗ the correct number of pictures to match the given numbers.

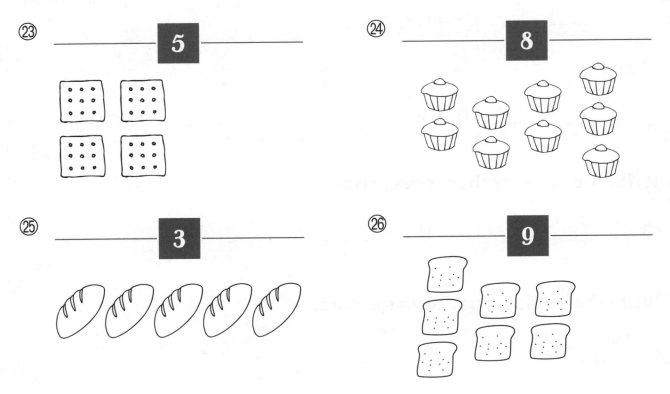

㉓ ____ **5** ____   ㉔ ____ **8** ____

㉕ ____ **3** ____   ㉖ ____ **9** ____

ISBN: 978-1-897164-29-7

More than: means count forward

2 more than 5 is 7.

Less than: means count backwards

1 less than 6 is 5.

Fill in the missing numbers.

㉗ 1, 2, ____ , ____ , 5

㉘ 4, 5, ____ , ____ , 8

㉙ 7, 6, ____ , ____ , 3

㉚ 10, 9, ____ , ____ , 6

㉛ 5, ____ , ____ , ____ , 9

㉜ 8, ____ , ____ , 5, ____

Colour the correct number of boxes. Then fill in the blanks.

㉝ 1 more than 6: ____

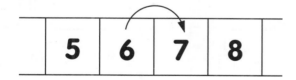

| 5 | 6 | 7 | 8 | |

㉞ 2 less than 5: ____

| | 3 | 4 | 5 | 6 |

㉟ 1 less than 4: ____

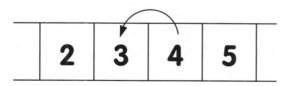

| | 2 | 3 | 4 | 5 |

㊱

2 more than 7 is ____ .

ISBN: 978-1-897164-29-7

Addition and Subtraction of 1

- Put 1 more item in a group and use words to describe addition.
- Take away 1 item from a group and use words to describe subtraction.

2 and 1 make 3. I have 3 eyes in all.

Count and write the number of items in each group. Then draw 1 more item and tell how many items there are in all.

① ◯ — 1 — ☐ in all

② ◯ — 1 — ☐ in all

③ ◯ — 1 — ☐ in all

④ ◯ — 1 — ☐ in all

ISBN: 978-1-897164-29-7

Draw the correct number of items to show the total. Then write the numbers to match the group of items.

⑤  and make

_____ and _____ make   _____

⑥  and make

_____ and _____ make   _____

⑦ and make

_____ and _____ make   _____

⑧  and make

_____ and _____ make   _____

ISBN: 978-1-897164-29-7

Count and write how many items there are in each group. Then put a cross ✗ on an item and tell how many items are left.

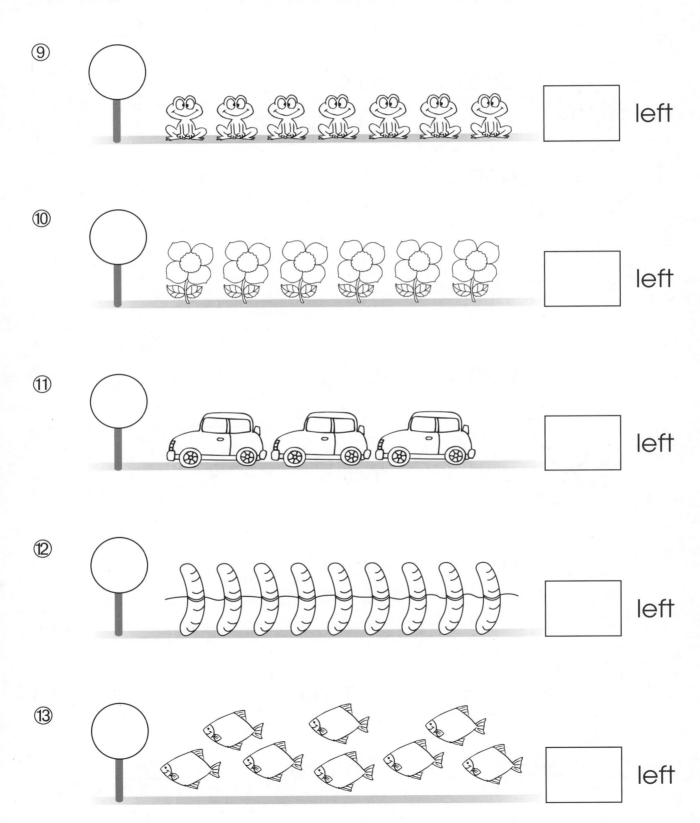

⑨ _____ left

⑩ _____ left

⑪ _____ left

⑫ _____ left

⑬ _____ left

ISBN: 978-1-897164-29-7

Cross out ✗ 1 item in each group.   Then fill in the blanks with numbers.

⑭  _____ take away _____ leaves _____

⑮ _____ take away _____ leaves _____

⑯  _____ take away _____ leaves _____

⑰ _____ take away _____ leaves _____

⑱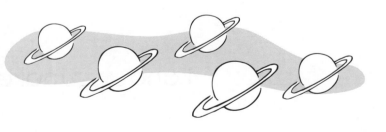

_____ take away _____ leaves _____ .

Addition and Subtraction Facts to 6

$3 + 2 = 5$
$3 - 2 = 1$

- Add or subtract 1-digit numbers with the help of pictures.
- Do addition and subtraction up to 6.
- Understand the use of "+", "−", and "=" to describe addition or subtraction problems.

I have 5 fish in all, and I have 1 more big fish than small fish.

Draw the correct number of pictures. Then complete the addition sentences.

① 2 more

3 and ____ make ____

② 2 more

2 and ____ make ____

③ 1 more

4 and ____ make ____

④ 3 more

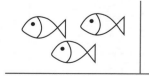

3 and ____ make ____

ISBN: 978-1-897164-29-7

Fill in the blanks with numbers to match the pictures.

⑤

$2 + \underline{\hphantom{000}} = \underline{\hphantom{000}}$

⑥

$\underline{\hphantom{000}} + \underline{\hphantom{000}} = \underline{\hphantom{000}}$

⑦

$\underline{\hphantom{000}} + \underline{\hphantom{000}} = \underline{\hphantom{000}}$

⑧

$\underline{\hphantom{000}} + \underline{\hphantom{000}} = \underline{\hphantom{000}}$

⑨

$\underline{\hphantom{000}} + \underline{\hphantom{000}} = \underline{\hphantom{000}}$

⑩

$\underline{\hphantom{000}} + \underline{\hphantom{000}} = \underline{\hphantom{000}}$

Draw your own pictures to match the addition sentences. Then find the answers.

⑪

$1 + 5 = \underline{\hphantom{000}}$

⑫

$3 + 3 = \underline{\hphantom{000}}$

ISBN: 978-1-897164-29-7

Cross out X the correct number of pictures. Then complete the subtraction sentences.

⑬ Cross out 1 fish.

3 take away _____ leaves _____

3 - _____ = _____

⑭ Cross out 2 pears.

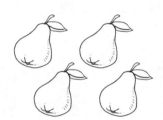

4 take away _____ leaves _____

4 - _____ = _____

⑮ Cross out 3 cats.

7 take away _____ leaves _____

7 - _____ = _____

⑯ Cross out 1 tree.

9 take away _____ leaves _____

9 - _____ = _____

ISBN: 978-1-897164-29-7

Steps to do word problems:

1st Read the problem once.
2nd Underline the key words, such as "in all" and "left".
3rd Write a number sentence.
4th Find the answer.

Complete the number sentences to match the pictures.

⑰

_____ + _____ = _____

⑱

_____ − _____ = _____

⑲

_____ − _____ = _____

⑳

_____ + _____ = _____

Help the cat solve the problems.

㉑ There are 🐟🐟 and 🐟🐟🐟🐟 . How many fish are there in all?

____ + ____ = ____

____ fish

㉒ *How many fish are left?*

_____ − _____ = _____

____ fish

ISBN: 978-1-897164-29-7

Addition and Subtraction Facts to 10

She has 7 rings in all.

- Add or subtract 1-digit numbers with or without the help of pictures.
- Do addition or subtraction up to 10.
- Do vertical addition or subtraction.

$$\begin{array}{r} 3 \\ +\ 4 \\ \hline 7 \end{array}$$

Fill in the blanks with numbers to match the pictures.

①

4 + _____ = _____

②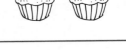

_____ + _____ = _____

③

_____ + _____ = _____

④

_____ + _____ = _____

⑤

_____ + _____ = _____

⑥

_____ + _____ = _____

ISBN: 978-1-897164-29-7

Find the answers with the help of the picture.

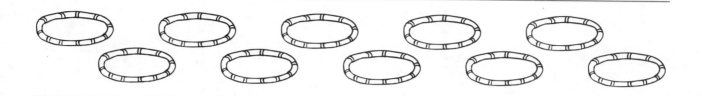

⑦ $3 + 5 =$ _____   ⑧ $4 + 2 =$ _____

⑨ $6 + 1 =$ _____   ⑩ $5 + 5 =$ _____

⑪ $3 + 4 =$ _____   ⑫ $8 + 1 =$ _____

⑬ $7 + 2 =$ _____   ⑭ $2 + 3 =$ _____

Draw 10 apples in the tree. Then find the answers with the help of the apples.

⑮ $4 + 5 =$ _____

⑯ $3 + 1 =$ _____

⑰ $2 + 6 =$ _____

⑱ $4 + 4 =$ _____

⑲ $5 + 2 =$ _____

⑳ $1 + 9 =$ _____

㉑ $3 + 3 =$ _____   ㉒ $2 + 4 =$ _____

㉓ $5 + 3 =$ _____   ㉔ $1 + 6 =$ _____

ISBN: 978-1-897164-29-7

Fill in the blanks with numbers to match the pictures.

㉕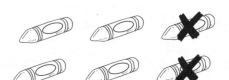

$\underline{6}$ – $\underline{2}$ = _____

㉖

_____ – _____ = _____

㉗

_____ – _____ = _____

㉘

_____ – _____ = _____

㉙

_____ – _____ = _____

㉚

_____ – _____ = _____

Find the answers with the help of the picture.

㉛ $9 - 4$ = _____

㉜ $8 - 5$ = _____

㉝ $6 - 1$ = _____

㉞ $9 - 7$ = _____

㉟ $10 - 3$ = _____

㊱ $8 - 4$ = _____

㊲ $8 - 2$ = _____

㊳ $7 - 3$ = _____

ISBN: 978-1-897164-29-7

Vertical addition or subtraction:

Remember to align the numbers on the **right-hand side**.

e.g.

$$
\begin{array}{r} 6 \\ + \ 4 \\ \hline 10 \end{array} \ \textbf{✗}
\qquad
\begin{array}{r} 6 \\ + \ 4 \\ \hline 10 \end{array} \ \textbf{✔}
\qquad
\begin{array}{r} 10 \\ - \ 3 \\ \hline 7 \end{array} \ \textbf{✗}
\qquad
\begin{array}{r} 10 \\ - \ 3 \\ \hline 7 \end{array} \ \textbf{✔}
$$

Find the answers.

㊴
$$\begin{array}{r} 5 \\ + \ 3 \\ \hline \end{array}$$

㊵
$$\begin{array}{r} 7 \\ - \ 4 \\ \hline \end{array}$$

㊶
$$\begin{array}{r} 9 \\ - \ 6 \\ \hline \end{array}$$

㊷
$$\begin{array}{r} 4 \\ + \ 4 \\ \hline \end{array}$$

㊸
$$\begin{array}{r} 6 \\ - \ 2 \\ \hline \end{array}$$

㊹
$$\begin{array}{r} 7 \\ + \ 3 \\ \hline \end{array}$$

㊺
$$\begin{array}{r} 5 \\ - \ 1 \\ \hline \end{array}$$

㊻
$$\begin{array}{r} 8 \\ + \ 1 \\ \hline \end{array}$$

㊼
$$\begin{array}{r} 10 \\ - \ 6 \\ \hline \end{array}$$

㊽

I had 10 rings at first, but now I only have these rings left. How many rings did I lose?

$$\begin{array}{r} 10 \\ - \ \boxed{} \\ \hline \boxed{} \end{array}$$

_____ rings

ISBN: 978-1-897164-29-7

More about Addition and Subtraction

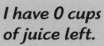

I have 0 cups of juice left.

$4 - 4 = 0$

- Add or subtract with 0.
- Do addition or subtraction up to 10.
- Do subtraction to get 0 as an answer.
- Use addition or subtraction to solve word problems.

Find the answers with the help of the picture.

① $\begin{array}{r} 3 \\ + 4 \\ \hline \end{array}$ ② $\begin{array}{r} 7 \\ + 1 \\ \hline \end{array}$ ③ $\begin{array}{r} 5 \\ + 2 \\ \hline \end{array}$

④ $\begin{array}{r} 5 \\ - 1 \\ \hline \end{array}$ ⑤ $\begin{array}{r} 4 \\ - 3 \\ \hline \end{array}$ ⑥ $\begin{array}{r} 9 \\ - 6 \\ \hline \end{array}$

⑦ $2 + 6 =$ _____   ⑧ $8 - 5 =$ _____

⑨ $4 + 3 =$ _____   ⑩ $7 - 5 =$ _____

⑪ $5 + 4 =$ _____   ⑫ $9 - 2 =$ _____

⑬ $3 + 2 =$ _____   ⑭ $8 - 3 =$ _____

⑮ $4 + 5 =$ _____   ⑯ $9 - 7 =$ _____

ISBN: 978-1-897164-29-7

Look at the pictures. Complete the number sentences.

⑰

$6 + 0 =$ _____

⑱

_____ $+ 0 =$ _____

⑲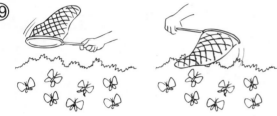

$7 - 0 =$ _____

⑳

$3 -$ _____ $=$ _____

㉑

_____ $+ 4 =$ _____

㉒

$5 -$ _____ $=$ _____

Find the answers.

㉓
$$\begin{array}{r} 9 \\ + \ 0 \\ \hline \end{array}$$

㉔
$$\begin{array}{r} 8 \\ - \ 0 \\ \hline \end{array}$$

㉕
$$\begin{array}{r} 6 \\ - \ 0 \\ \hline \end{array}$$

㉖ $1 + 0 =$ _____

㉗ $5 - 0 =$ _____

㉘ $4 - 0 =$ _____

㉙ $0 + 7 =$ _____

㉚ $3 - 0 =$ _____

㉛ $2 + 0 =$ _____

ISBN: 978-1-897164-29-7

Look at the pictures. Complete the number sentences.

③②
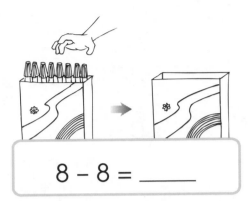

8 – 8 = _____

③③

5 – 5 = _____

Find the answers.

③④
$$\begin{array}{r} 3 \\ -\ 3 \\ \hline \end{array}$$

③⑤
$$\begin{array}{r} 4 \\ -\ 4 \\ \hline \end{array}$$

③⑥
$$\begin{array}{r} 6 \\ -\ 6 \\ \hline \end{array}$$

③⑦ 8 – 8 = _____

③⑧ 7 – 7 = _____

③⑨ 9 – 9 = _____

④⓪ 1 – 1 = _____

④① *I have 2 bones. If I eat 2 bones, how many bones will I have left?*

$$\begin{array}{r} 2 \\ -\ \boxed{} \\ \hline \boxed{} \end{array}$$

_____ bones

④② *David the Dog has 5 bones. If he gives me all his bones, how many bones will he have left?*

$$\begin{array}{r} 5 \\ -\ \boxed{} \\ \hline \boxed{} \end{array}$$

_____ bones

ISBN: 978-1-897164-29-7

"**+**": means "add" or "plus" "**–**": means "take away" or "minus" "**=**": means "equal to"	Addition key words: in all, total Subtraction key words: fewer, more...than, left

Solve the problems.

㊸ Judy has 5 red balls and 2 green balls. How many balls does Judy have in all?

_____ ⊕ _____ = _____   _____ balls

㊹ Mrs. Green has 7 big apples and 3 small apples. How many more big apples than small apples does she have?

_____ ◯ _____ = _____   _____ more

㊺ There are 4 boys and 4 girls playing in a park. How many children are there in the park?

_____ ◯ _____ = _____   _____ children

㊻

> *I bought 5 popsicles. They all melted. How many popsicles do I have now?*

_____ ◯ _____ = _____

_____ popsicles

ISBN: 978-1-897164-29-7

Numbers 1 to 20

- Recognize the numbers from 1 to 20.
- Count forward or backward from a given number.
- Tell whether a number is even or odd.

I have 13 blueberries.

Count and write the numbers.

①

②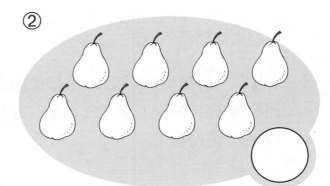

③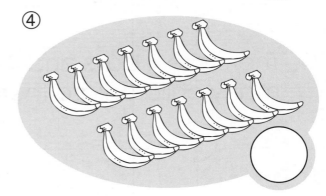

④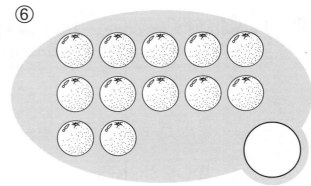

⑤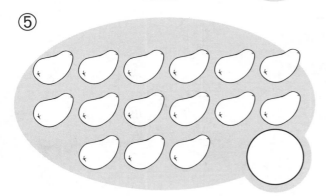

⑥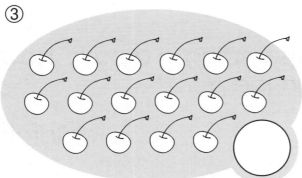

ISBN: 978-1-897164-29-7

Write the number that comes after.

⑦ 15 _____   ⑧ 12 _____   ⑨ 19 _____

⑩ 13 _____   ⑪ 10 _____   ⑫ 16 _____

Write the number that comes before.

⑬ _____ 9   ⑭ _____ 17   ⑮ _____ 12

⑯ _____ 16   ⑰ _____ 10   ⑱ _____ 5

Fill in the missing numbers.

⑲ (12) (13) (   ) (   ) (   ) (17) (   ) (19)

⑳ (19) (18) (   ) (   ) (15) (   ) (   ) (12)

㉑ 7 8 _____ _____ 11 _____ _____ 14

㉒ 9 8 _____ _____ 5 _____ _____ 2

㉓ 10 11 _____ _____ _____ 15 _____ 17

㉔ 16 15 _____ _____ _____ 11 _____ 9

ISBN: 978-1-897164-29-7

Put the numbers in order from least to greatest.

㉕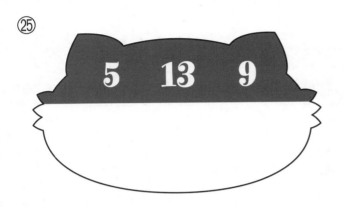

㉖

㉗ 4, 10, 8, 5

In order: _____

㉘ 3, 7, 11, 2

In order: _____

Draw arrows on the number lines. Then fill in the blanks.

㉙ 2 less than 14 is _____ .

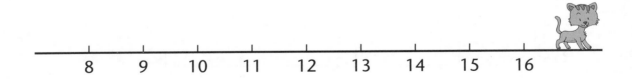

㉚ 3 more than 12 is _____ .

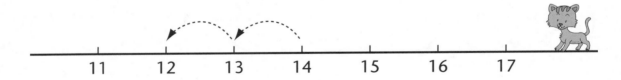

㉛ 3 less than 11 is _____ .

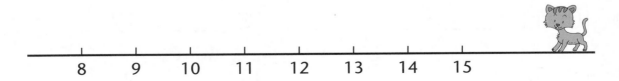

ISBN: 978-1-897164-29-7

There are two ways to tell whether a number is **even** or **odd**.

- By doing

  Circle every two items. If there are no items left, the number is even; otherwise, it is odd.

- By looking

  Even number: a number ending in 0, 2, 4, 6, or 8

  Odd number: a number ending in 1, 3, 5, 7, or 9

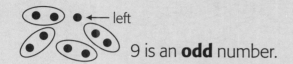 ← left

9 is an **odd** number.

14 ← ending in 4

14 is an **even** number.

Draw the correct number of dots to match each number. Then circle ◯ every two dots and tell whether the number is odd or even.

㉜

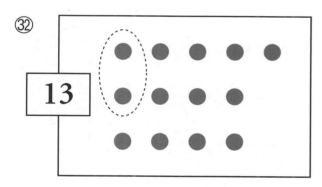

13

13 is an _____ number.

㉝

12

12 is an _____ number.

Look at the ending of each number. Then colour the even numbers yellow and the odd numbers red.

㉞

3

9

19

10

6

8

20

14

18

15

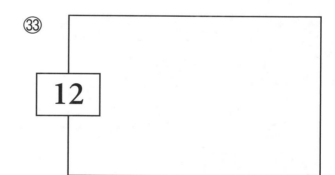

ISBN: 978-1-897164-29-7

Numbers 21 to 100

- Recognize the numbers from 21 to 100.
- Understand the place value of each digit in a 2-digit number.
- Compare numbers.
- Tell whether a given number is an even or odd number.

2 tens and 7 ones are 27.

Count and write the numbers.

①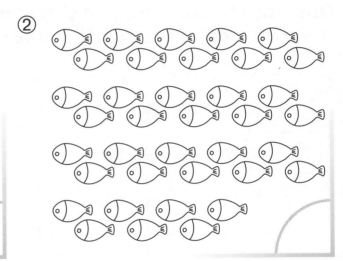

②

③

④

ISBN: 978-1-897164-29-7

Complete the hundreds chart.

⑤

1	2	3	4	5			8		10
	12	13		15		17		19	20
		23	24		26	27	28		
31	32		34		36			39	40
	42			45		47	48		
		53			56	57		59	60
61			64	65			68	69	
71		73		75	76			79	
	82	83			86	87			90
	92	93		95		97			100

Write the number that comes after.

⑥ 56 _____   ⑦ 72 _____   ⑧ 89 _____

Write the number that comes before.

⑨ _____ 94   ⑩ _____ 67   ⑪ _____ 40

Fill in the missing numbers.

⑫ 64 65 _____ _____ 68 69 _____ _____ 72

⑬ 88 89 _____ 91 _____ _____ 94 _____ 96

⑭

44 43   41   37

ISBN: 978-1-897164-29-7

Count and write the numbers.

⑮

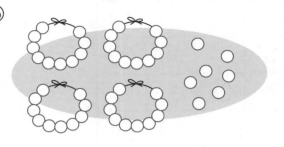

Tens	Ones

= _____ tens and _____ ones

= _____ + _____

⑯

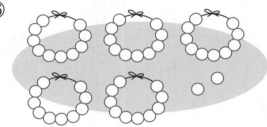

Tens	Ones

= _____ tens and _____ ones

= _____ + _____

Fill in the blanks.

⑰ 65 = _____ tens and _____ ones

⑱ 15 = _____ + 5

⑲ 38 = _____ tens and _____ ones

⑳ 46 = 40 + _____

㉑ 97 = _____ tens and _____ ones

㉒ 87 = _____ + _____

㉓ _____ = 5 tens and 3 ones

㉔ _____ = 30 + 4

㉕ _____ = 4 tens and 9 ones

㉖ _____ = 60 + 1

Colour the greater number in each pair.

㉗ 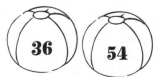 36 54

㉘  69 85

㉙  23 20

ISBN: 978-1-897164-29-7

Odd or even numbers:

If the digit in the ones place of a number is
- 1, 3, 5, 7, or 9, it is an **odd** number.
- 2, 4, 6, 8, or 0, it is an **even** number.

e.g.   **45**   **96**
        ↑   ↑
   odd number   even number

45 is an odd number and 96 is an even number.

Fill in the blanks with the help of the number lines.

③⓪ 3 less than 91 is _____ .   ③① 4 more than 27 is _____ .

87 88 89 90 91 92

③② 2 less than 62 is _____ .   ③③ 3 more than 78 is _____ .

Look at the numbers on the bone. Answer the questions.

③④ How many even numbers are there? What are they?

_____ ; _____

③⑤ Which odd number is greater than 80?

_____

63   70   54   82   16   91   78   47

Counting by 1's, 2's, 5's, or 10's

- Count forward by 1's, 2's, 5's, or 10's.
- Count backward by 1's, 2's, or 5's from 20.
- Find out the best way to do counting.

6 groups of 5 are 30. I have 30 fingers in all.

Fill in the missing numbers.

① 85 86 ___ ___ 89 ___ ___ ___ 93 94

② 12 11 ___ ___ 8 ___ ___ 5 ___ 3

③ 19 18 ___ 16 ___ ___ 13 ___ ___ 10

④ 64 65 ___ ___ 68 ___ ___ ___ 72 73

Read what the animals say. Write the numbers.

⑤    *Count forward by 1's from 47 to 58.*

_____

⑥    *Count backward by 1's from 16 to 6.*

_____

ISBN: 978-1-897164-29-7

Circle ◯ the objects in groups of 2. Then fill in the blanks.

⑦

Count by 2's: _____ , _____ , _____ , _____ , _____ , _____ ,

_____ , _____

There are _____ acorns.

⑧

Count by 2's: _____

There are _____ bells.

⑨

Count by 2's: _____

There are _____ ants.

Fill in the blanks.

⑩ 3 twos = _____   ⑪ 4 twos = _____

⑫ 9 twos = _____   ⑬ 8 twos = _____

⑭ 74 76 78 _____ _____ _____ 86 _____ 90

⑮ 36 34 32 _____ _____ 26 _____ _____ 20

ISBN: 978-1-897164-29-7

Fill in the blanks with the help of the picture.

⑯

a. 1 five is _____ .

b. 2 fives are _____ .

c. 3 fives are _____ .

d. 4 fives are _____ .

e. 5 fives are _____ .

f. 6 fives are _____ .

g. 7 fives are _____ .

h. 8 fives are _____ .

i. 9 fives are _____ .

j. 10 fives are _____ .

Fill in the missing numbers.

⑰ 25   30   _____   40   _____   _____   55   _____

⑱ 60   65   _____   _____   80   _____   90   _____

⑲ 80   75   _____   _____   _____   55   _____   45

⑳   (15)   _____   _____   30   _____   _____   45

ISBN: 978-1-897164-29-7

Circle ⬭ the objects in groups of 10. Count and write the numbers.

㉑

_____ stars

㉒

_____ hearts

Fill in the blanks.

㉓ 4 tens are _____ .

㉔ 7 tens are _____ .

㉕ 3 tens are _____ .

㉖ 9 tens are _____ .

㉗ _____ tens are 80.

㉘ _____ tens are 50.

Circle ⬭ the correct words. Then write the numbers.

㉙

There are 10 bowls in a stack.
The best way to count the
bowls is by 2's 5's 10's . I
have _____ bowls in all.

ISBN: 978-1-897164-29-7

Money

- Identify the names and state the values of coins.
- Compare and order coins by size and value.
- Write money amounts to 20¢.
- Add and subtract money amounts to 10¢.

Draw lines to match the coins with their names. Then write the values of the coins.

①

- Toonie ; $ _____
- Loonie ; $ _____
- Quarter ; _____ ¢
- Dime ; _____ ¢
- Nickel ; _____ ¢
- Penny ; _____ ¢

Look at the coins above again. Answer the questions.

② Which coin is the biggest in size? _____

③ Which coin is the smallest in size? _____

   ISBN: 978-1-897164-29-7

Circle ◯ the coin with a greater value in each pair.

④

⑤

⑥

⑦

⑧

⑨

Put the coins in order from the one with the greatest value to the one with the least. Write the letters.

⑩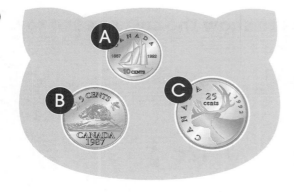

In order: _____

⑪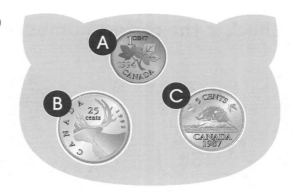

In order: _____

⑫

In order: _____

⑬

In order: _____

ISBN: 978-1-897164-29-7

Find the value of each group of coins.

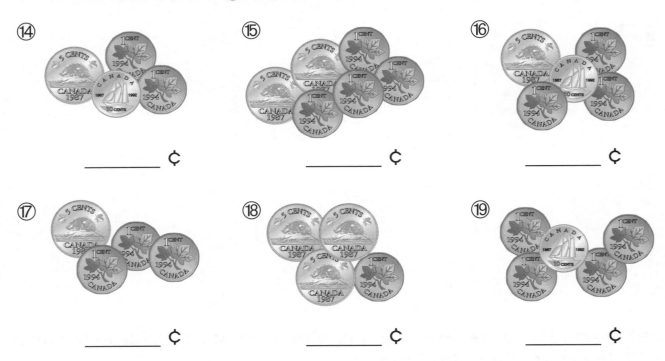

⑭ _____ ¢

⑮ _____ ¢

⑯ _____ ¢

⑰ _____ ¢

⑱ _____ ¢

⑲ _____ ¢

Check ✔ the correct number of coins to show the cost of each toy.

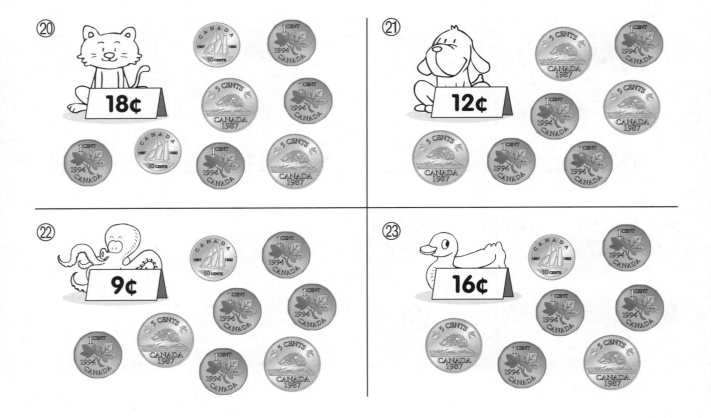

⑳ **18¢**

㉑ **12¢**

㉒ **9¢**

㉓ **16¢**

ISBN: 978-1-897164-29-7

Use addition to find the total and subtraction to find the change.

- Buy  and

$$
\begin{array}{r}
5 \ \text{¢} \\
+ \ 3 \ \text{¢} \\
\hline
8 \ \text{¢}
\end{array}
$$

Total: __8¢__

- Pay  for

$$
\begin{array}{r}
10 \ \text{¢} \\
- \ 3 \ \text{¢} \\
\hline
7 \ \text{¢}
\end{array}
$$

Change: __7¢__

Look at the pictures. Answer the questions.

Happy Birthday **5¢**

4¢

3¢

8¢

㉔ Tom wants to buy a bear and a card for his mom. How much does he need to pay?

_____ ¢

$$
\begin{array}{r}
\text{¢} \\
+ \quad \text{¢} \\
\hline
\text{¢}
\end{array}
$$

㉕ How much more does a robot cost than a butterfly?

_____ ¢

㉖ *If I pay for a robot with a dime, what is my change?*

_____ ¢

ISBN: 978-1-897164-29-7

Measuring with Non-standard Units

- Measure and describe length, height, and area using non-standard units.
- Compare and order objects based on the measurement in non-standard units.

How many pencils or nails long is each item? Count and write the numbers to complete the sentences.

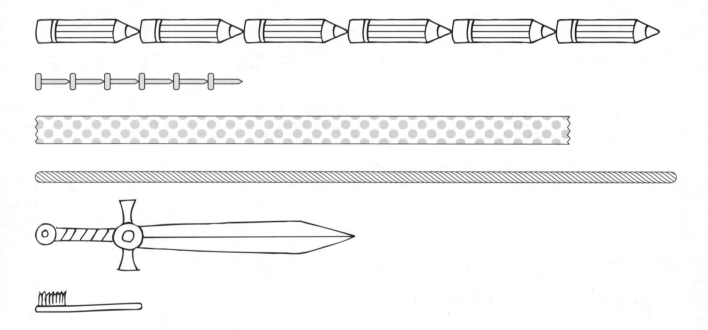

① The ribbon is about _____ pencils or _____ nails long.

② The rope is about _____ pencils or _____ nails long.

③ The sword is about _____ pencils or _____ nails long.

④ The toothbrush is about _____ pencil or _____ nails long.

ISBN: 978-1-897164-29-7

Draw pictures to match the descriptions.

⑤ A fish that is 3 pencils long and a rope that is a bit longer than 4 pencils

⑥ A sandwich that is 1 paper clip thick and a box that is a bit thinner than 2 paper clips

⑦ A tree that is 3 floors high and a building that is 1 floor taller than the given building

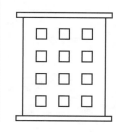

Which is the better unit for each measurement? Circle ◯ the correct answer.

⑧ The length of a long aisle: combs   belts

⑨ The height of a coffee table: straws   screws

ISBN: 978-1-897164-29-7

What is the distance between the objects? Write the numbers on the lines or circle ⃝ the correct pictures or numbers.

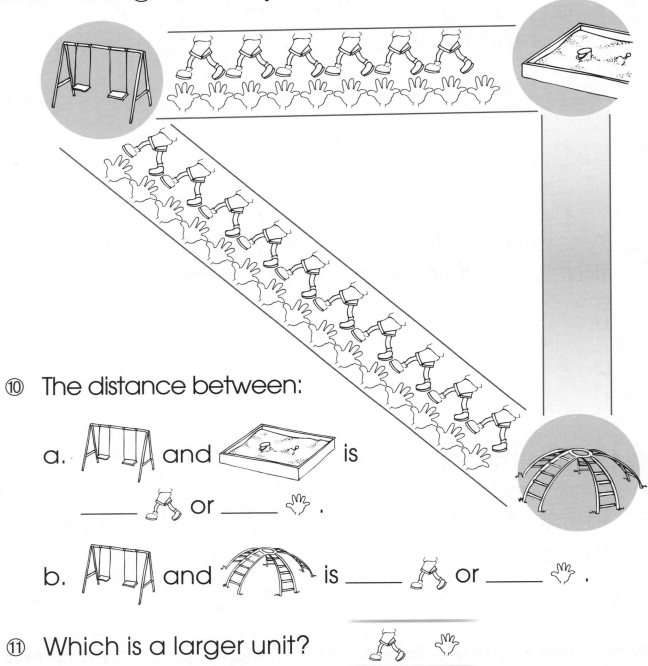

⑩ The distance between:

a. and is

_____ or _____ 🖐 .

b. and is _____ or _____ 🖐 .

⑪ Which is a larger unit?

⑫ The distance between and is

about 2 / 6 / 10 or 10 / 15 / 30 🖐 .

ISBN: 978-1-897164-29-7

Look at the pictures.   Find the number of stickers needed to cover each picture and circle ◯ the correct answer.

⑬

_____ ♡

_____ 🏠

_____ 👔

_____ ✏️

⑭   ♡ 🏠 👔 ✏️   covers the most space.

⑮   It takes about _____ ♡ to cover a 👔 .

Follow the pattern to draw lines over the monster. Then answer the question.

⑯
> *How many squares are needed to cover me?*

About _____ squares

ISBN: 978-1-897164-29-7

Colour the heavier one.

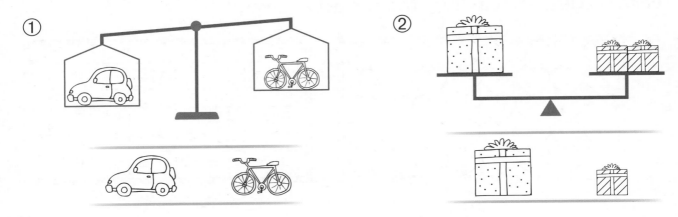

Put the things in order. Write the letters.

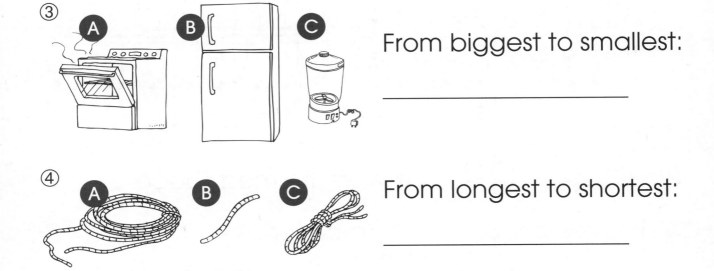

From biggest to smallest:

_____

From longest to shortest:

_____

Count and write the numbers. Then write the numbers in words.

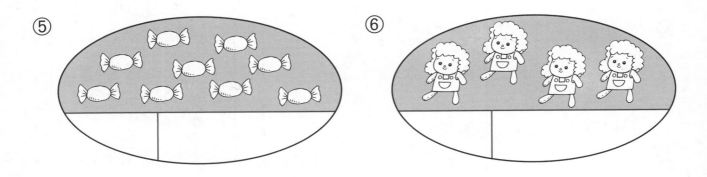

ISBN: 978-1-897164-29-7

Put the numbers in order from greatest to smallest.

⑦ **53 24 14 49**   _____

⑧ **84 90 9 48**   _____

⑨ **77 70 17 71**   _____

Circle ◯ the things. Then count them by 2's, 5's, or 10's and write the numbers.

⑩ in groups of 2

⑪ in groups of 10

_____ stars

_____ hearts

⑫ in groups of 5

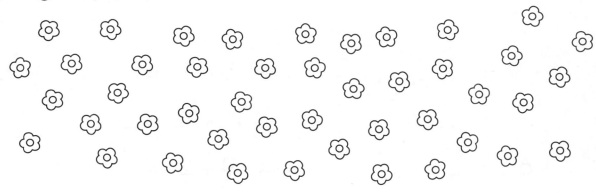

_____ flowers

ISBN: 978-1-897164-29-7

Look at the picture. Answer the questions.

⑬

a. The ribbon is about ____ pencils long.

b. Draw a line under the ribbon which is a bit shorter than 6 pencils.

c. Draw a stick under the line which is a bit longer than 2 pencils.

Find the answers.

⑭
$$\begin{array}{r} 7 \\ + 4 \\ \hline \end{array}$$

⑮
$$\begin{array}{r} 6 \\ - 2 \\ \hline \end{array}$$

⑯
$$\begin{array}{r} 1 \\ + 8 \\ \hline \end{array}$$

⑰
$$\begin{array}{r} 9 \\ + 2 \\ \hline \end{array}$$

⑱ $16 - 9 =$ ____

⑲ $5 + 7 =$ ____

⑳ $8 - 3 =$ ____

㉑ $4 + 4 =$ ____

㉒ $7 + 6 =$ ____

㉓ $9 + 2 =$ ____

㉔ $14 - 8 =$ ____

㉕ $10 - 3 =$ ____

ISBN: 978-1-897164-29-7

See how many tickets are needed to trade the toys. Help the children solve the problems.

8 tickets

4 tickets

15 tickets

9 tickets

㉖ Trade and :

_____ = _____   _____ tickets

㉗ Trade and :

_____ = _____   _____ tickets

㉘ How many more tickets are needed to trade a robot than a ball?

_____ = _____   _____ more

㉙ How many fewer tickets are needed to trade a snake than a robot?

_____ = _____   _____ fewer

㉚ Do the girls have enough tickets to trade a giraffe?

I have 7 tickets.

I have 4 tickets.

They   have / do not have enough tickets to trade a giraffe.

ISBN: 978-1-897164-29-7

Look at the coins that the children have. Complete the record and answer the questions.

Lucy   Paul   Katie

③ Lucy: ____ dimes and ____ nickel

Paul: _____

Katie: _____

loonie
dime
penny
toonie
quarter
nickel

③ Who have nickels?

_____

③ How much does Lucy have?   ____ ¢

③ How many coins does Katie have?   ____ coins

③

If I buy  *6¢* *with a dime, what is my change?*

Lucy

____ ¢

ISBN: 978-1-897164-29-7

How many shapes are needed to cover each sticker? Write the number. Then circle ◯ the correct answers.

㊱ a.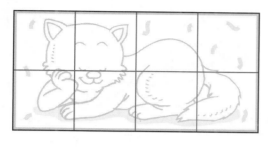

b.

_____ ▭ are needed.

_____ ▯ are needed.

c. ▢ / ▯ covers more space.

㊲ a.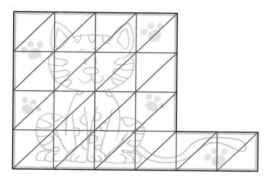

b.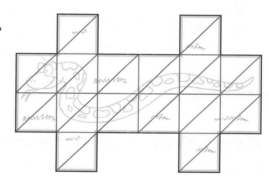

_____ ◺ are needed.

_____ ◺ are needed.

c. / has a greater area.

Which thing is better for measuring the area of each thing? Write the letter.

㊳

A 51¢

B Zoo Animals

a. a table mat _____

b. a mattress _____

ISBN: 978-1-897164-29-7

Capacity

- Estimate and compare capacities of containers.
- Find the capacity of a container by using non-standard units.

> *I can hold more than you.*

Colour the one with a greater capacity.

①

②

③

Colour the one with the greatest capacity.

④

⑤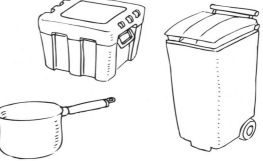

⑥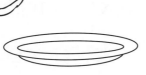

⑦

ISBN: 978-1-897164-29-7

Look at the pictures. Circle ◯ the correct answers to complete the sentences.

⑧

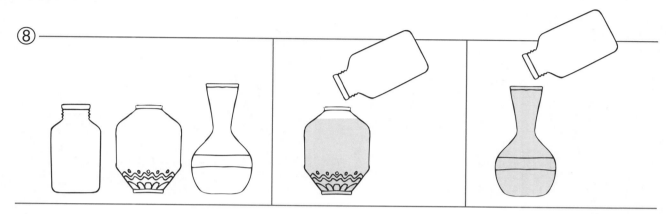

a. ⌣ can hold **more / less** water than ⬜ .

b. ⬜ and ⬺ have   the same capacity / different capacities .

⑨

a. ⬜ can hold **more / less** water than ⬜ .

b. ⬜ ⬜ ⬜   has the greatest capacity.

ISBN: 978-1-897164-29-7

See how many cups or pails are needed to hold the water in each container. Write the numbers. Then complete the sentences.

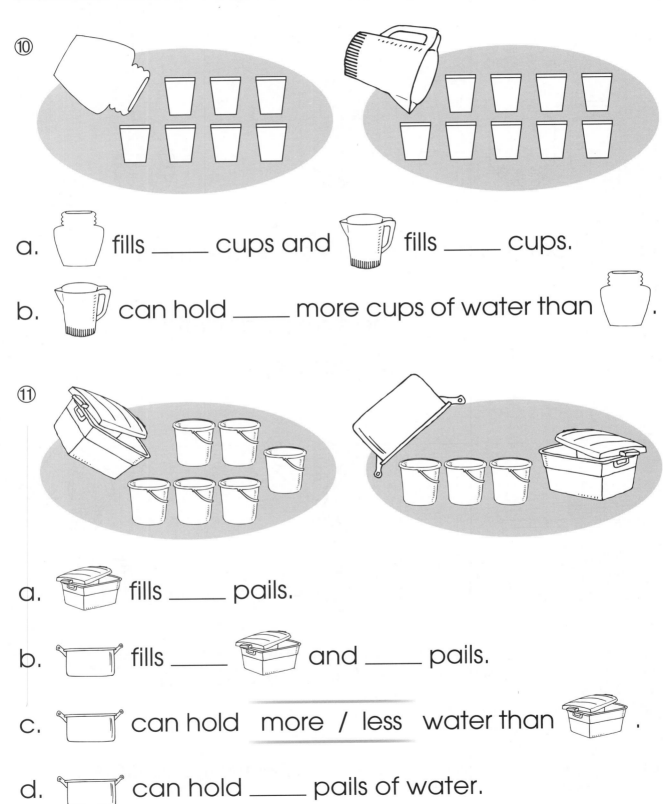

⑩

a. fills _____ cups and fills _____ cups.

b. can hold _____ more cups of water than .

⑪

a. fills _____ pails.

b. fills _____ and _____ pails.

c. can hold   more / less   water than .

d. can hold _____ pails of water.

ISBN: 978-1-897164-29-7

Choose the most appropriate thing to measure the capacity of the container on the left. Check ✔ the letters.

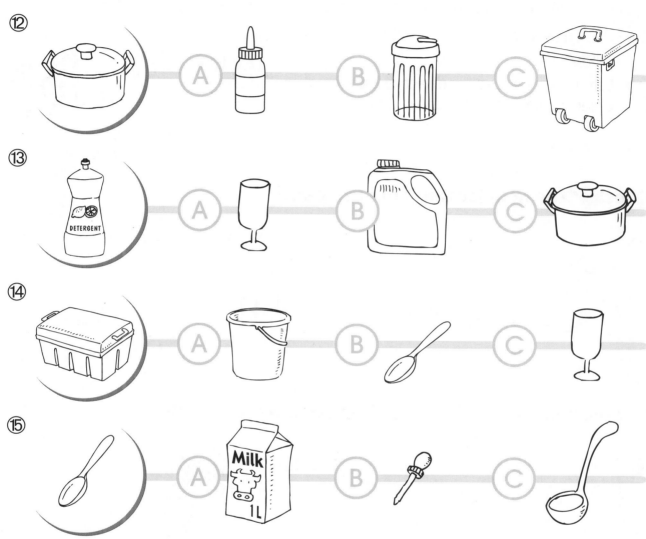

Circle ◯ the correct number to complete what the can says.

⑯

It takes 6 boxes of juice to fill me up. If my brother can hold 2 more boxes, my brother can hold 4 / 2 / 8 *boxes of juice.*

ISBN: 978-1-897164-29-7

Mass

- Compare and order masses of objects.
- Describe masses of objects by using relative terms.
- Estimate, measure, and record masses of objects using non-standard units.

You're heavier.

Check ✔ the heavier thing in each pair.

①

②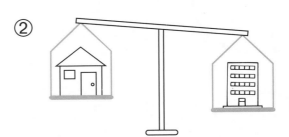

Put the things in order from lightest to heaviest. Write 1 to 3.

③

⑤

④

ISBN: 978-1-897164-29-7

Draw lines to match the things about the same mass.

⑥

Look at the pictures. Fill in the blanks with "lighter" or "heavier".

⑦

a. A pineapple is _____ than an apple.

b. A cherry is _____ than an apple.

⑧

a. A basketball is _____ than a beach ball.

b. A basketball is _____ than a bowl.

ISBN: 978-1-897164-29-7

How many blocks are needed to balance each thing? Count and write the number. Then answer the questions.

⑨

a. The house has the same weight as _____ blocks.

b. The mug has the same weight as _____ blocks.

c. The piggy bank has the same weight as _____ blocks.

d. The doll has the same weight as _____ blocks.

⑩ Which thing is the heaviest? _____

⑪ Which thing is the lightest? _____

Look at the pictures above again. Then draw the correct number of blocks on the correct side to balance the objects.

⑫

 ISBN: 978-1-897164-29-7

Look at the pictures. Fill in the blanks.

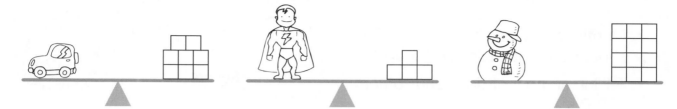

⑬ The car has the same weight as ＿＿ blocks.

⑭ The figurine has the same weight as ＿＿ blocks.

⑮ The snowman has the same weight as ＿＿ blocks.

⑯ ＿＿＿ figurines are needed to balance the car.

⑰ It takes ＿＿＿ car(s) and ＿＿＿ figurine(s) to balance the snowman.

Read what the mouse says. Help him draw the correct number of fish to balance the cat.

⑱

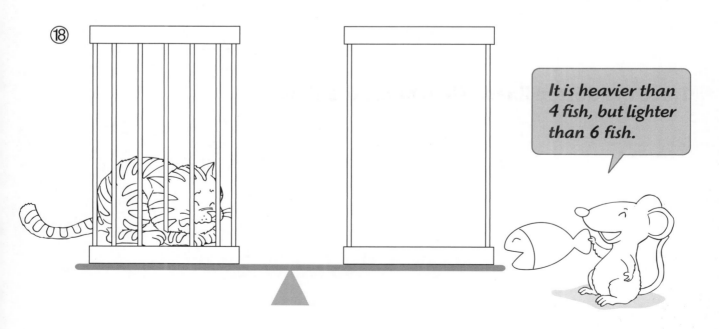

It is heavier than 4 fish, but lighter than 6 fish.

ISBN: 978-1-897164-29-7

2-D Shapes

- Identify and describe common 2-D shapes such as circles and squares.
- Tell the number of sides and corners of 2-D shapes.

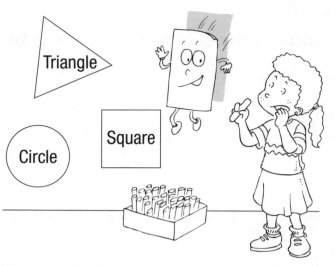

Draw lines to match the shapes with their names.

①

Circle •

Hexagon •

Pentagon •

Rectangle •

Square •

Triangle •

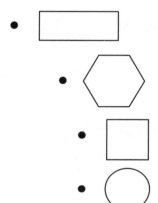

Trace the dotted lines. Then name the shapes.

②

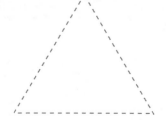

③

④

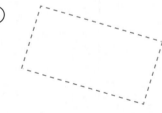

_____   _____   _____

ISBN: 978-1-897164-29-7

Trace each shape on the left on a piece of tracing paper. Then cut it out and compare it with each of the shaded shape on the right. Describe the shapes.

wider   narrower   taller   shorter
bigger   smaller   the same

⑤

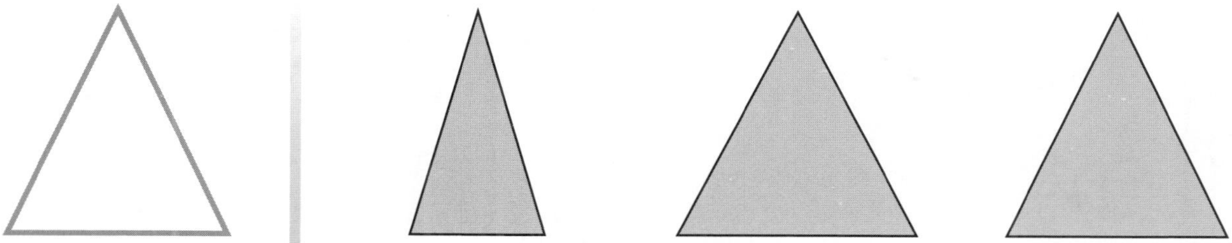

⑥

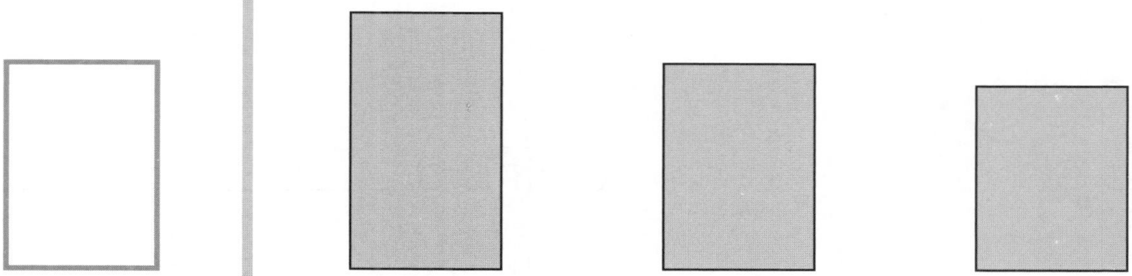

⑦

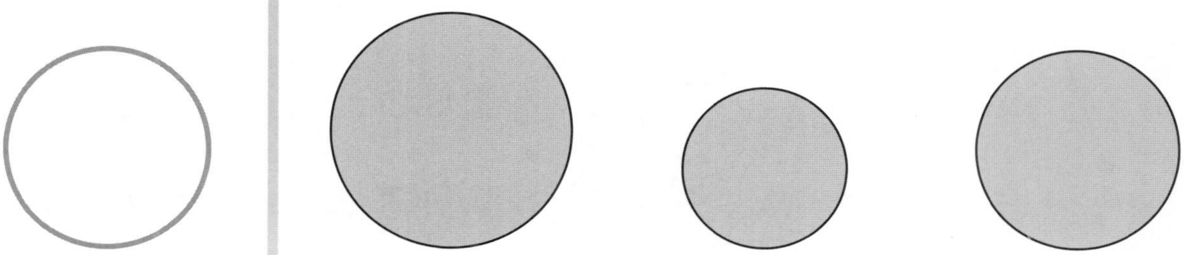

ISBN: 978-1-897164-29-7

Join the dots in order. Then name the shapes and write the numbers.

⑧

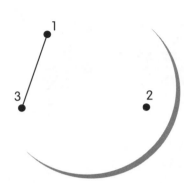

a. It is a _____ .

b. It has _____ sides and _____ corners.

⑨

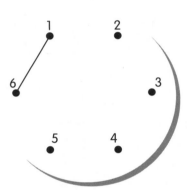

a. It is a _____ .

b. It has _____ sides and _____ corners.

⑩

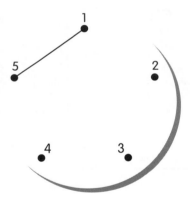

a. It is a _____ .

b. It has _____ sides and _____ corners.

⑪

It is a _____ .

It has _____ sides and _____ corners.

ISBN: 978-1-897164-29-7

Colour the pentagons red and the hexagons yellow.

⑫

Read what the girl says. Help her draw the robot.

⑬

> My robot's head is a rectangle. His eyes are pentagons and his nose is a hexagon. His ears are triangles and his mouth is a circle.

ISBN: 978-1-897164-29-7

More about Shapes

- Identify shapes in a given design.
- Identify and complete symmetrical shapes.
- Use fractions to describe parts of a whole.

We are all symmetrical.

Trace the dotted lines. Then write the names of the shapes that you can see in each design.

①

_____

_____

②

_____

_____

③

_____

_____

④

_____

_____

ISBN: 978-1-897164-29-7

Colour the symmetrical pictures.

⑤

Draw the missing parts to make each picture symmetrical.

⑥

ISBN: 978-1-897164-29-7

Trace the dotted lines and colour one part of each shape. Then tell how much is coloured.

⑦

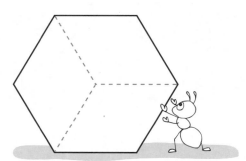

_____ fourth

⑧

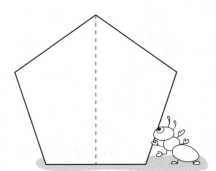

_____ half

⑨

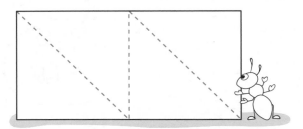

_____ third

⑩

_____

⑪

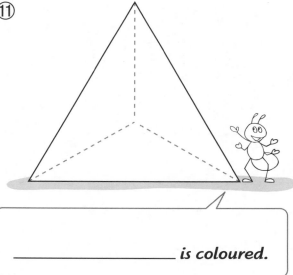

_____ _is coloured._

⑫

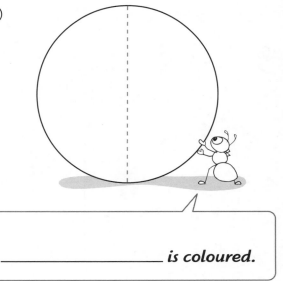

_____ _is coloured._

ISBN: 978-1-897164-29-7

Look at the pictures.   Fill in the blanks.

⑬

   a. George has _____ of a sandwich.

   b. Bob has _____ of it.

⑭

   a. Tiffany has _____ of a cupcake.

   b. Leo has _____ of it too.

⑮

   a. Chris has _____ of a pizza.

   b. Nancy has _____ of it.

Read what the nutcracker says. Is he correct? Explain.

⑯

One quarter of my sword is shaded.

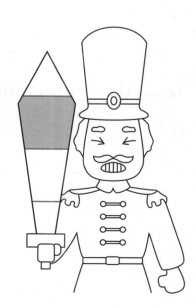

_____

_____

_____

ISBN: 978-1-897164-29-7

3-D Solids

- Identify and complete common 3-D solids.
- Identify the faces of 3-D solids.
- Describe similarities and differences between common objects and 3-D solids.

Draw lines to match the solids with their names.

①

Cone •

Cube •

Cylinder •

Prism •

Sphere •

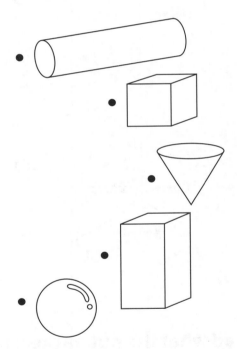

Trace the dotted lines to complete the solids. Then name them.

②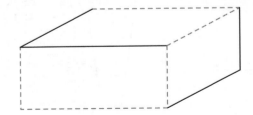

③

_____   _____

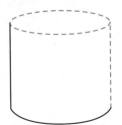 ISBN: 978-1-897164-29-7

What solid does each object look like? Write the name of the 3-D solid. Then draw one thing which has the same shape as the one given.

④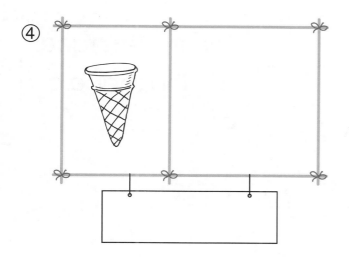

⑤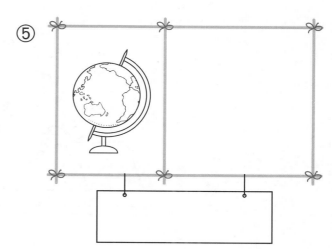

⑥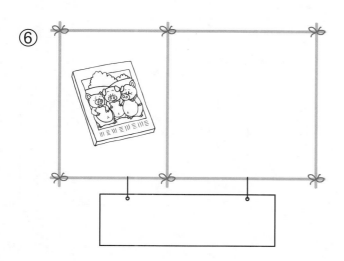

⑦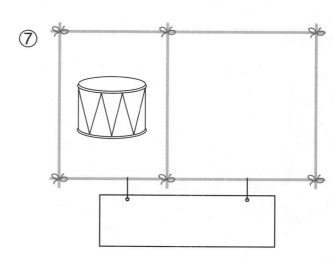

⑧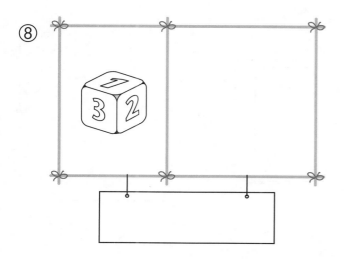

⑨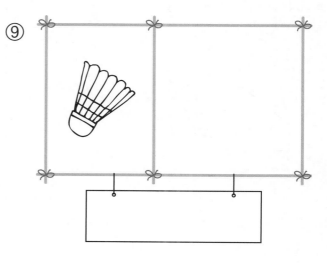

ISBN: 978-1-897164-29-7

See how Bruce traces the 3-D solids. Draw and name the traced faces.

⑩

The traced face is in the shape of a _____ .

⑪

⑫ _____

⑬ _____

⑭ _____

ISBN: 978-1-897164-29-7

Compare everyday objects and 3-D solids to find their **differences** and **similarities**.

The bottle looks like a cylinder, except that it gets thinner at the top.

A sphere can **roll**.

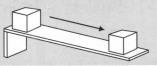

A cube can **slide**.

What 3-D solids do these objects look like? Name the solids and describe them.

⑮

It looks like a _____ , _____

_____ .

⑯

It looks like a _____ , _____

_____ .

⑰

It looks like a _____ , _____

_____ .

Read what the clown says. Help him colour the solids.

⑱ *Colour the solids that can roll and slide.*

ISBN: 978-1-897164-29-7

Directions (1)

- Use words such as "in front of", "behind", "left", and "right" to describe positions.
- Complete a picture to show the position of things.

I'm on your right, Mom.

And, I'm on your left.

Look at the picture. Circle ◯ the correct answers.

① Alex is in front of   Judy / Tom / Eric   .

② Judy is behind   Bill / Alex / Sue   .

③ Eric is   in front of / behind   Sue.

④ Bill is   in front of / behind   Tom.

⑤ There are   2 / 3 / 5   children in front of Judy.

⑥ There are   4 / 3 / 2   children behind Alex.

ISBN: 978-1-897164-29-7

Colour the correct pictures to match the sentences. Then fill in the blanks with "in front of" or "behind" to describe the coloured pictures.

⑦ The dog is in front of the cage and the cat is behind the cage.

a.

b. The cage is _____ the cat.

c. The cage is _____ the dog.

⑧ The house is in front of the cat and the tree is behind the cat.

a.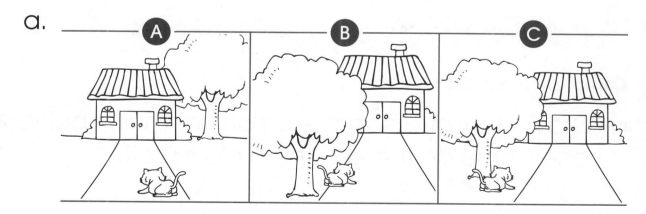

b. The cat is _____ the house.

c. The tree is _____ the house.

ISBN: 978-1-897164-29-7

Look at the pictures. Fill in the blanks with "left" or "right".

⑨

a. The two-eyed alien is on the _____ of Tom.

b. The one-eyed alien is on the _____ of Tom.

c. The one-eyed alien has a stethoscope in his _____ hand.

⑩ a. Ray has an umbrella in his _____ hand.

b. The cactus is on the _____ of Ray.

c. Ray is on the _____ of the cactus.

Complete the picture.

⑪ Draw two carrots on the left of the small rabbit and one apple on the left of the big rabbit.

ISBN: 978-1-897164-29-7

Read the clues to find the names of the girls. Write the names in the boxes and fill in the blanks with "in front of", "behind", "left", or "right".

⑫ • Mabel and Cindy are on the right of Tammy.
   • Sue is on the left of Tammy.
   • Cindy is on the right of Mabel.

⑬ There are many shapes _____ the girls.

⑭ There is a window _____ one of the girls.

⑮ Tammy is on the _____ of Mabel.

⑯ Cindy is on the _____ of Sue.

Look at the picture. Complete the sentences.

⑰ The girl is _____ the boy.

⑱ The boy has a balloon in his _____ hand.

⑲ The girl has a lollipop in her _____ hand.

ISBN: 978-1-897164-29-7

Directions (2)

- Use words such as "inside", "outside", "over", and "under" to describe positions.
- Complete a picture to show the positions of things.

Although I'm inside a cage under you, you can't reach me.

Look at the pictures. Circle ◯ the correct answers.

①

a. Amy is   inside / outside   the room.

b. A cat is   inside / outside   the room.

②

a. A bee is inside / outside the jar.

b. A butterfly is   inside / outside   the jar.

③

a. Mom is going inside / outside .

b. Brother Ant and Sister Ant are playing ball inside / outside .

ISBN: 978-1-897164-29-7

Look at the picture. Fill in the blanks with "over" or "under". Then draw things to complete the picture.

④

a. Lucy is _____ the roof.

b. A toy helicopter is flying _____ the roof.

c. A pail is _____ the bridge.

d. Louis is _____ the umbrella.

e. A dog is crawling _____ the stairs.

f.   A ball is thrown _____ the bridge.

g. Draw a bird flying under the clouds.

h. Draw a rainbow over the clouds.

ISBN: 978-1-897164-29-7

Read each sentence. Colour the correct picture. Then fill in the blank to give one more description of the coloured picture.

⑤ A cat is under the table and it is outside the box.

The box is _____ the table.

⑥ A fly is flying over the food dome and a cake is inside the dome.

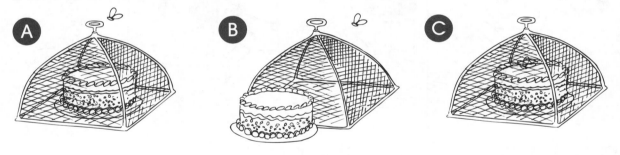

The fly is flying _____ the cake.

⑦ The outside of the box has stripes and a frog is jumping over the box.

The _____ of the box has dots.

ISBN: 978-1-897164-29-7

Look at the picture. Fill in the blanks.

⑧   There are 3 balls _____ the basket.

⑨   The fairy is flying _____ the lion.

⑩   There is a ball _____ the lion's left paw.

⑪   The mouse has his hands _____ his head.

⑫   The lion is _____ the cage.

Help the mouse write two sentences with the given words to describe the picture above.

⑬   stars, over: _____

_____

⑭   mouse, inside: _____

_____

ISBN: 978-1-897164-29-7

Temperatures

- Recognize the names and characteristics of the four seasons.
- Use simple words to describe different weather conditions.
- Read and record temperatures in degree Celsius (°C) with a thermometer.

Four-Season Show

Match the pictures with the seasons. Write the letters.

①

A

B

C

D

E

F

G

H

Spring: _____   Summer: _____

Fall: _____   Winter: _____

ISBN: 978-1-897164-29-7

Which season does each picture show? Write the name of the season. Then put the pictures in order starting with spring. Write 1 to 4.

②

a. _____

b. _____

c. _____

d. _____

Fill in the blanks with the given words and draw pictures in the boxes to complete the "Weather Facts".

hottest	coldest	warm
cold	snowy	sunny

Weather Facts

③

Spring: _____ , cool to _____

Summer: _____ , the _____ season

Fall: cool to _____

Winter: _____ , the _____ season

Circle ◯ the correct words to complete what the children say. Then help the children check ✔ the correct clothing.

④

> I can build snowmen with my sister today because the temperature is
>
> low / high enough to keep the snow there. Which outfit should I wear?

 A
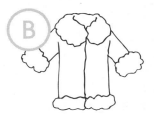 B
 C

⑤

> Although the temperature is low / high , I can't play outside because
>
> it is rainy. But it will be much hotter / colder next month, so I will go
>
> to the beach then! Which outfit should I wear if I go to the beach?

 A
 B
 C

Circle ◯ the best description for each season.

⑥ Spring   coldest / getting warmer / getting colder

⑦ Fall   warmest / getting warmer / getting colder

ISBN: 978-1-897164-29-7

Temperature is measured in **degree Celsius (°C)**.

When the temperature gets higher, the weather gets hotter.

25°C

5°C

Record the temperatures. Then circle ○ the best word to describe each temperature.

⑧ 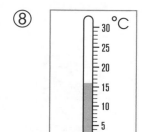 _____ °C

cold

mild

hot

⑨ _____ °C

cold

mild

hot

⑩ 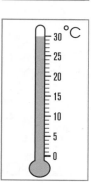 _____ °C

cold

mild

hot

⑪ _____ °C

cold

mild

hot

Read what the girl says. Help her colour the thermometer to show the temperature.

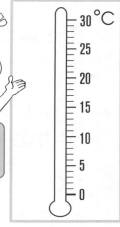

⑫ *Yesterday's temperature was 23°C. Today's temperature is 4°C higher than that of yesterday. What is today's temperature?*

_____ °C

ISBN: 978-1-897164-29-7

23

Days, Weeks, Months, and Time

Half past 7

- Name the days of the week.
- Put the months of the year in order and read the date on a calendar.
- Read and write time to the hour and half-hour.
- Draw clock hands to show time.

See what Eric will do next week. Help him answer the questions.

① Eric will play ball on _____ .

② On _____ and _____ , Eric will play computer games.

③ On how many days will Eric read books? _____ days

④ On which day of the week will he have two things to do? _____

⑤ What will he do on the first day of the week? _____

⑥ How many days are there in a week? _____ days

ISBN: 978-1-897164-29-7

Put the months in the correct order starting with January. Write 1 – 12.

⑦ ____ May   ____ September   ____ July

____ June   ____ October   ____ February

____ March   ____ December   _1_ January

____ April   ____ November   ____ August

Fill in the missing information on Jill's calendar. Then answer the questions.

⑧

OCT ___ ___ ___ R   's Calendar

SUN	MON			THU		SAT
	1	2	3	④		6
7			10		12	13
🎂Mom	15			18	19	
	22	23				27
28			🎃			

◯ Field Trip

⑨ The first day of this month is a _____ .

⑩ What is the date of Jill's field trip?   _____

⑪ When is the birthday of Jill's mom?   _____

⑫ Jill will buy a costume 2 days before Halloween. What is the date?   _____

ISBN: 978-1-897164-29-7

**See what Nancy did yesterday. Help her write the times in 2 ways.
Then put the pictures in the correct order.**

⑬ **A**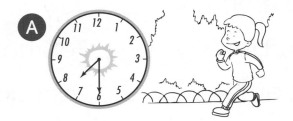

half past _____

_____ : 30

B

_____

_____ : _____

C

_____

_____ : _____

D

_____

_____ : _____

⑭ In order: _____ , _____ , _____ , _____

Use "nearly" or "a little after" to write the times.

⑮

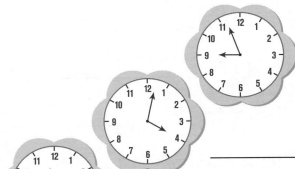

_____ _____ o'clock

_____

_____

ISBN: 978-1-897164-29-7

 The long hand is the **minute hand**. The short hand is the **hour hand**.

It is half-past 8. The long hand points to 6 and the short one points to the middle of 8 and 9.

Draw the clock hands to show the times.

⑯ 9:00

⑰ 3:30

⑱ 10:30

⑲ 4:30

⑳ 7:00

㉑ 5:00

Help Cindy the Clock complete the clock face and draw the clock hands to show the time.

㉒ *It is a little after half-past 3 right now.*

ISBN: 978-1-897164-29-7

Patterns

- Identify the pattern of a group of things.
- Continue a pattern by drawing or colouring.
- Create a pattern with the given objects.
- Find patterns in hundreds charts.

Can you see the pattern on my crown?

Put a check mark ✔ in the circle if each group of pictures follows a pattern; otherwise, put a cross ✗.

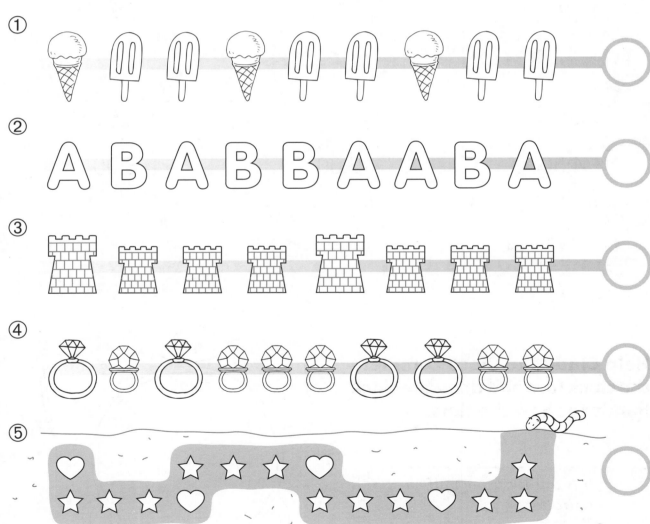

①

② A B A B B B A A B A

③

④

⑤

ISBN: 978-1-897164-29-7

Draw the next two pictures.

⑥  _____ _____

⑦ 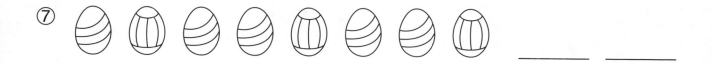 _____ _____

⑧ _____ _____

⑨ _____ _____

Cross out ✗ one picture in each group so that the pictures follow a pattern.

⑩

⑪

⑫

ISBN: 978-1-897164-29-7

Draw the missing picture in each pattern. Then use each set of pictures to create a pattern different from the one above the line.

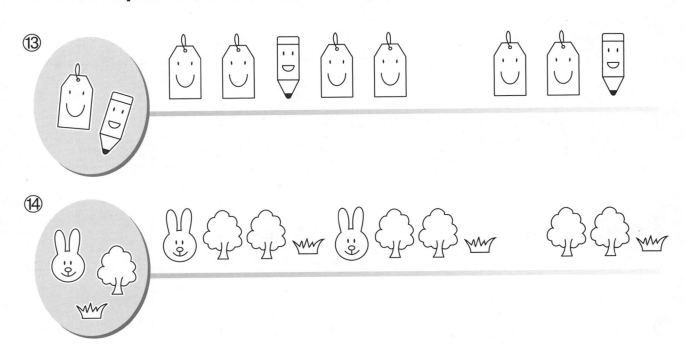

Trace the dotted lines to complete the patterns.

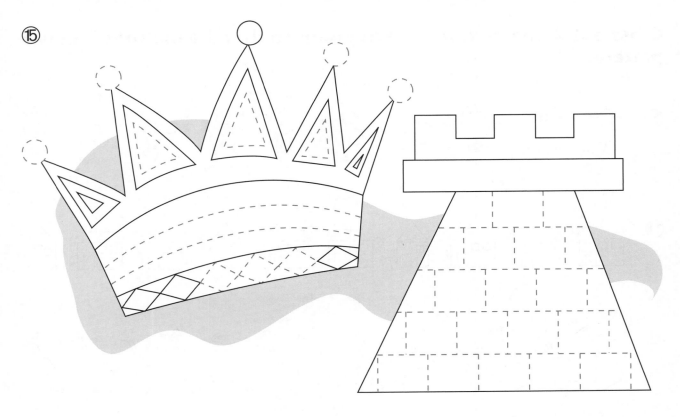

ISBN: 978-1-897164-29-7

Hundreds charts:

a chart with 10 rows, 10 columns, and 100 boxes, each containing a number from 1 to 100 arranged in order

10 columns

1	2	3	4	5	6	7	8	9	10
11	12	13	14	15	16	17	18	19	20
21	22	23	24	25	26	27	28	29	30
31	32	33	34	35	36	37	38	39	40
41	42	43	44	45	46	47	48	49	50
51	52	53	54	55	56	57	58	59	60
61	62	63	64	65	66	67	68	69	70
71	72	73	74	75	76	77	78	79	80
81	82	83	84	85	86	97	88	89	90
91	92	93	94	95	96	97	98	99	100

10 rows

Fill in the missing numbers in the hundreds chart. Colour the numbers to continue the pattern of the shaded boxes. Then answer the question.

⑯

1		3				7			
								19	
	23		25		27				
41									
51			55		57				
61									70
	73	74				78	79		
	82	83			86	87			90
91		94	95						

⑰

Look at the ones place of the coloured and shaded numbers. What pattern do you see?

Tens	Ones
2	5

_____

Organizing Data

- Organize objects into categories by sorting.
- Use a variety of recording methods to display data.

Sort the items in two ways. Count and write the numbers.

①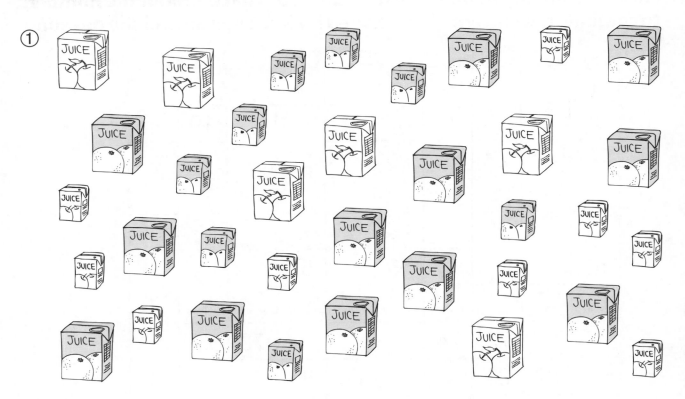

A **By flavour**	
Flavour	Number of boxes
Apple	
Orange	

B **By size**	
Size	Number of boxes
Big	
Small	

ISBN: 978-1-897164-29-7

Sue has a collection of stickers. Help her sort her stickers in two ways.
Use tally marks ||||| to record the data.

②

A By type	
Picture	Number of stickers
Animal	||||| ||||| ||
Plant	

B By shape	
Shape	Number of stickers
Circle	
Square	

ISBN: 978-1-897164-29-7

The children drew their favourite fast food on the board. Show their preferences. Colour a circle for each food item that you see and cross out ✗ each picture that you have counted.

③

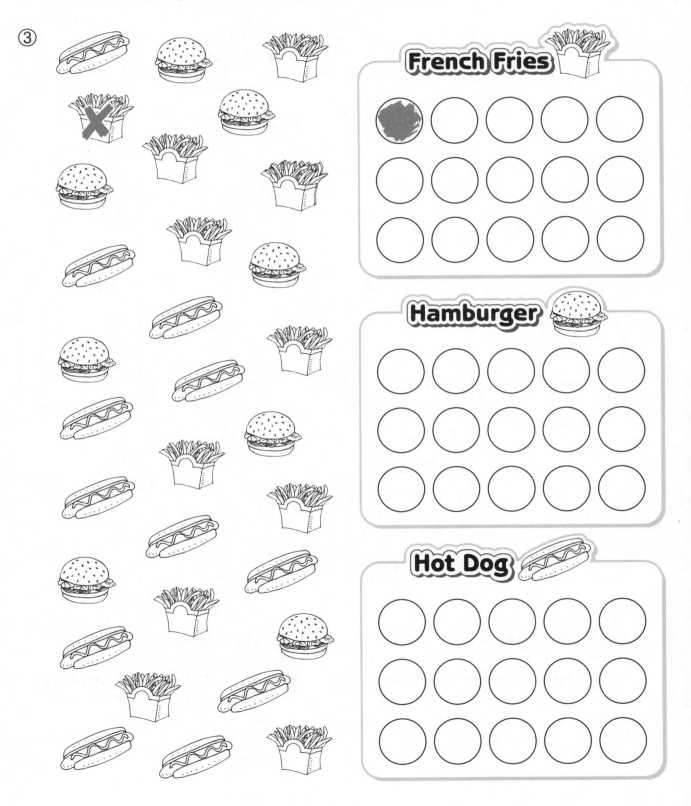

ISBN: 978-1-897164-29-7

Help Jenny sort her things into 3 groups. Write the rules. Colour a circle for each item you see and cross out ✗ each picture that you have counted.

④

Look at the cards above. Answer Jenny's question.

⑤ *What thing do I have the most?*

_____

ISBN: 978-1-897164-29-7

Pictographs

- Read pictographs and use comparative words to describe the data.
- Make pictographs to display data.

Most girls like dogs.

That's not true. Most girls like cats.

Look at the pictograph. Circle ◯ the correct answers.

Fruits in the Basket

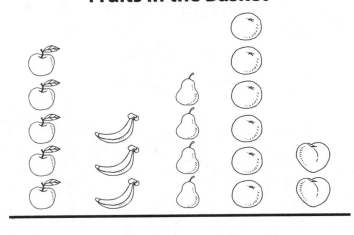

① There are   more / fewer   peaches than apples.

② There are   more / fewer   bananas than pears.

③ There are   2 / 3 / 4   more oranges than bananas.

④ There are   2 / 3 / 4   fewer peaches than oranges.

⑤ There are   5 / 6 / 7   kinds of fruits in the basket.

ISBN: 978-1-897164-29-7

Look at the pictograph. Answer the questions.

Favourite Sports in Mrs. Smith's Class

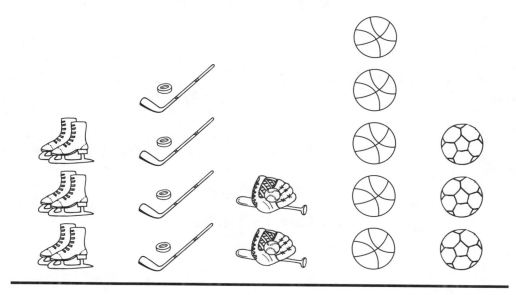

⑥ How many children like hockey?   ____ children

⑦ How many children like soccer?   ____ children

⑧ How many more children like hockey than baseball?   ____ more

⑨ Which sport do most children like?   _____

⑩ If 2 girls like basketball, how many boys like basketball?   ____ boys

⑪
> *I'm in Mrs. Smith's class. I don't like ball games.*
> *Do you know which sport is my favourite?*

_____

ISBN: 978-1-897164-29-7

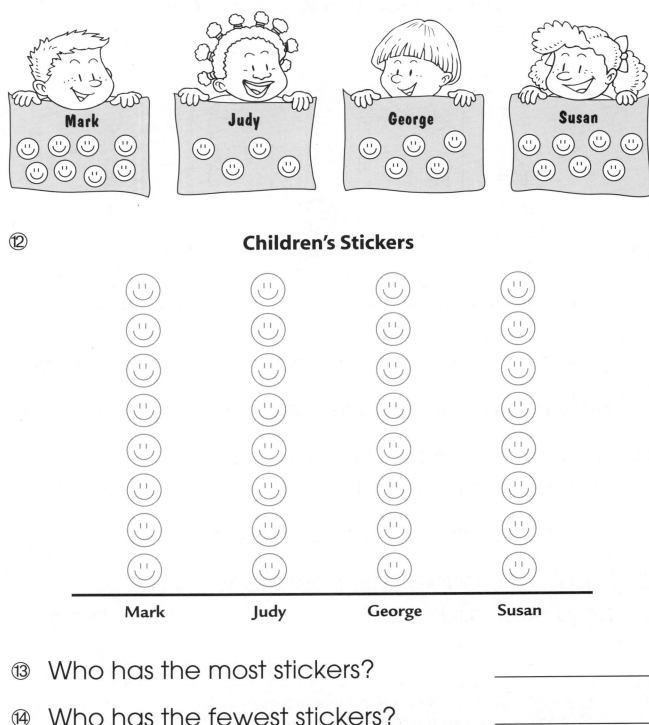

See how many stickers the children have. Help them colour the pictograph to show the information. Then answer the questions.

⑫ **Children's Stickers**

| Mark | Judy | George | Susan |

⑬ Who has the most stickers? _____

⑭ Who has the fewest stickers? _____

⑮ How many more stickers does Susan have than George? _____ more

ISBN: 978-1-897164-29-7

See how many fish the cats have. Help them colour the pictograph to show the information. Then answer the questions.

⑯ **Fish that Each Cat Has**

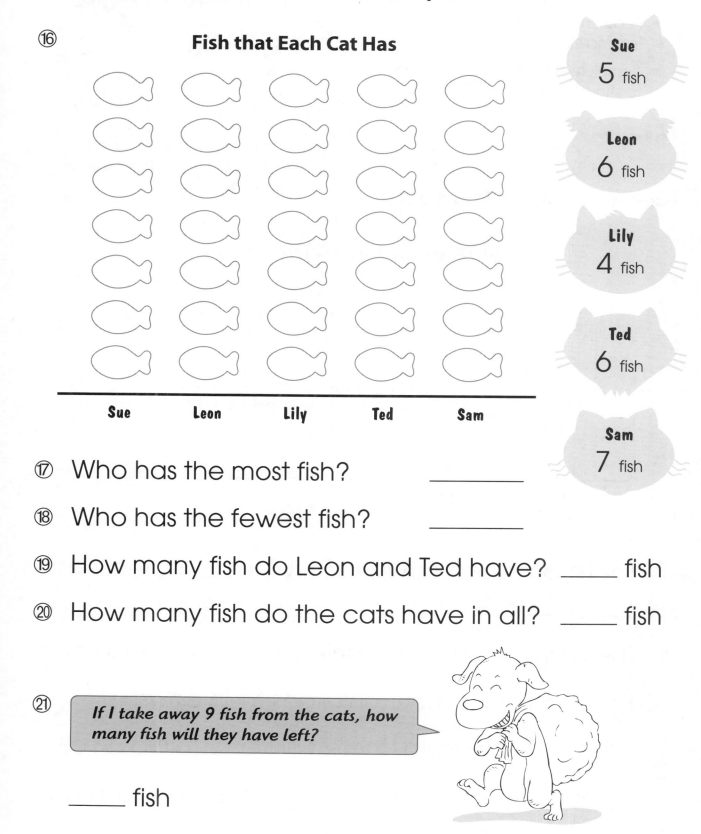

Sue
5 fish

Leon
6 fish

Lily
4 fish

Ted
6 fish

Sam
7 fish

⑰ Who has the most fish? _____

⑱ Who has the fewest fish? _____

⑲ How many fish do Leon and Ted have? ____ fish

⑳ How many fish do the cats have in all? ____ fish

㉑ *If I take away 9 fish from the cats, how many fish will they have left?*

_____ fish

ISBN: 978-1-897164-29-7

Concrete Graphs

- Read and describe data presented in concrete graphs.
- Complete or make concrete graphs to show the data.

Food on the table

There are 2 hamburgers, 4 hot dogs, 5 chicken nuggets, and 3 pieces of cheese.

Look at the graph. Fill in the blanks.

Animals on Mr. Smith's Farm

① There are _____ cows, _____ pigs, _____ hens, and _____ ducks.

② There are _____ kinds of animals on Mr. Smith's Farm.

③ There are _____ more chickens than cows.

④ If 5 piglets are born, there will be _____ pigs in all.

⑤ If each hen lays 3 eggs, _____ eggs are laid in all.

ISBN: 978-1-897164-29-7

See how the children in Mrs. Green's class come to school. Use the graph to answer the questions.

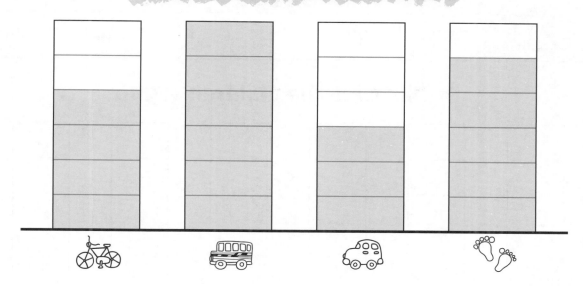

How Children Come to School

⑥ How many children come to school

   a. by bike?   _____ children

   b. on foot?   _____ children

⑦ How many more children come to school by school bus than by car? _____ more

⑧ If 2 girls come to school on foot, how many boys come to school on foot? _____ boys

⑨ By which way do most children come to school?   _____

⑩
> I need to wear a helmet when I go to school. By which way do I go to school?

_____

ISBN: 978-1-897164-29-7

See what drinks the children in Mrs. Taylor's class want to have. Colour to complete the graph and answer the questions.

Drink	Milk	Juice	Hot Chocolate	Pop	Slush	Water
No. of Children	||||	++++			|||	++++ ||	||||

⑪ **Drinks that the Children Want**

⑫ How many children like

a. juice? _____ children

b. water? _____ children

⑬ How many children are there in Mrs. Taylor's class? _____ children

⑭ *In which season do you think I did this survey, summer or winter? Why?*

_____

ISBN: 978-1-897164-29-7

See how many combos Uncle Bill wants to order for the party. Help him colour the concrete graph to show his order. Then answer the questions.

⑮ **Combos to Be Ordered**

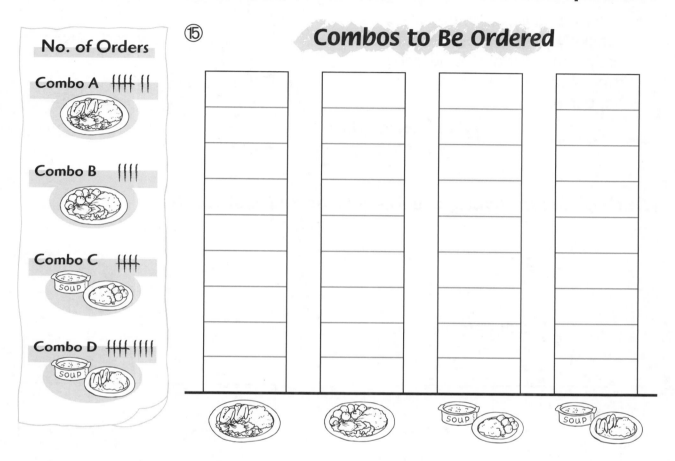

No. of Orders	
Combo A	☰☰ ‖
Combo B	‖‖‖
Combo C	☰
Combo D	☰☰ ‖‖‖

⑯ How many more Combo D's will Uncle Bill order than Combo B's?   _____ more

⑰ Which combo will he order the most?   _____

⑱ How many combos will be ordered in all?   _____ combos

⑲ *If I take away all the combos with chicken wings, how many combos do I get?*

_____

ISBN: 978-1-897164-29-7

Probability

- Use words such as "impossible", "unlikely", "less likely", "more likely", and "certain" to describe the likelihood of something happening.

I'll be bigger than you one day.

Impossible!

Which of the following are likely to occur? Colour them.

① ② ③ ④

ISBN: 978-1-897164-29-7

Use "impossible" or "certain" to describe each pair of pictures.

⑤

a. _____   b. _____

⑥

a. _____   b. _____

⑦

a. _____   b. _____

⑧

a. _____   b. _____

ISBN: 978-1-897164-29-7

Read what the children say. Then use "impossible", "unlikely", "likely", and "certain" to describe the chances.

⑨ *I've just had a big dinner, but I'll be hungry after one minute.*

_____

⑩ *My brother has a bad cold and Mom has just taken him to the doctor's. My brother will feel better soon afterwards.*

_____

⑪ *I'll finish two bottles of water in my outing tomorrow.*

_____

⑫ It is _____ that I have a big plate of seafood for breakfast.

⑬ It is _____ that I have two sausages and one egg for breakfast.

⑭ It is _____ that I finish eating breakfast in an hour.

ISBN: 978-1-897164-29-7

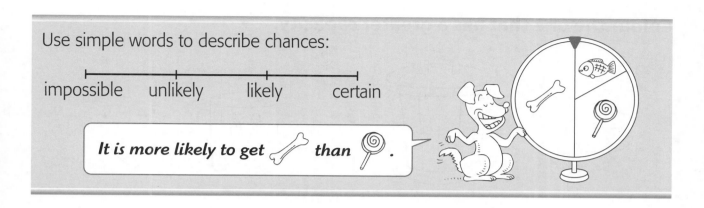

Use simple words to describe chances:

impossible   unlikely   likely   certain

It is more likely to get 🦴 than 🍭 .

Look at the pictures. Fill in the blanks with "more" or "less".

⑮

a. It is _____ likely to land on 🍦 than 🧁 .

b. It is _____ likely to land on 🧁 than 🍡 .

⑯

a. It is _____ likely to pick a ♡ than a ◎ .

b. It is _____ likely to pick a ✩ than a ◎ .

Colour the spinner to match what the mouse says.

⑰

It is more likely to land on yellow than green.

ISBN: 978-1-897164-29-7

Colour the one that has a greater capacity.

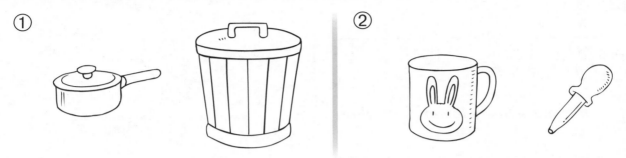

① ②

Write the number of blocks needed to balance each model. Then answer the questions.

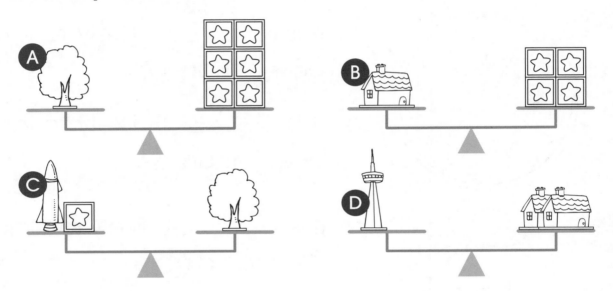

③

	as heavy as
A	☆
B	☆
C	☆
D	☆

④ Which model is the heaviest?

_____

⑤ Which model is the lightest?

_____

⑥ How many blocks are needed to balance 2 **C** ?

_____ blocks

ISBN: 978-1-897164-29-7

Trace and name each shape. Then count and write the number of sides and corners that it has.

circle   hexagon   pentagon   rectangle   square   triangle

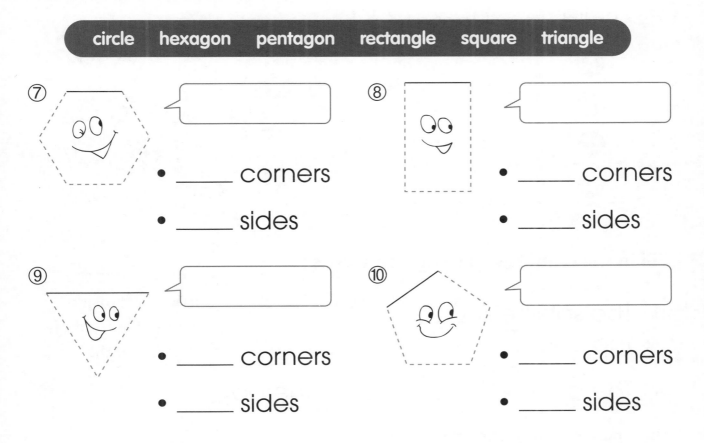

⑦
- _____ corners
- _____ sides

⑧
- _____ corners
- _____ sides

⑨
- _____ corners
- _____ sides

⑩
- _____ corners
- _____ sides

Colour the symmetrical shapes.

⑪

ISBN: 978-1-897164-29-7

Look at the picture and name the solids.

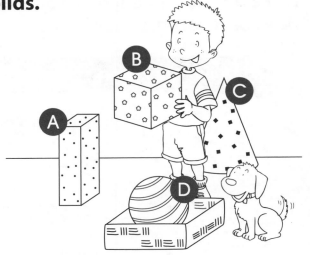

⑫

Solid	Name
A	
B	
C	
D	

Fill in the blanks with the given words.

over   under
inside   outside
behind   in front of
left   right

⑬ The sphere is _____ the cube.

⑭ The cone is _____ the boy.

⑮ The dog is on the _____ of the boy.

⑯ The cube is _____ the boy.

⑰ The sphere is _____ the basket.

Draw things to complete the picture.

⑱ • a sun over the tree

  • a flower on the right of the tree

  • a girl in front of the tree

ISBN: 978-1-897164-29-7

Look at the pictures. Name the seasons. Then record the temperatures.

⑲

_____ ; ____ °C

⑳

_____ ; ____ °C

㉑

_____ ; ____ °C

㉒

_____ ; ____ °C

Look at Tim's schedule. Fill in the blanks.

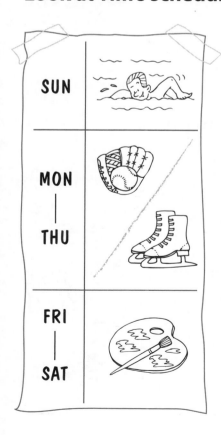

㉓ Tim has painting lessons on _____ and _____ .

㉔ He has a swimming lesson on _____ .

㉕ What activity does Tim have on the first day of the week?

_____

㉖ How many days a week does he have two activities?

____ days

Write the times in two ways. Then match them with the correct pictures.

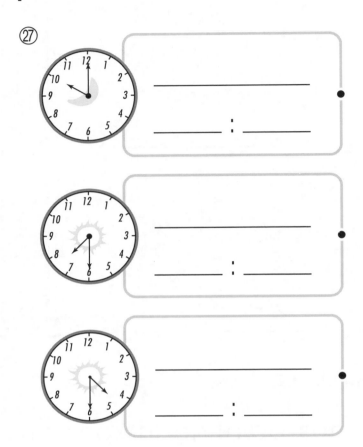

㉗

_____

_____ : _____

_____

_____ : _____

_____

_____ : _____

Find the pattern in each group. Draw the missing pictures.

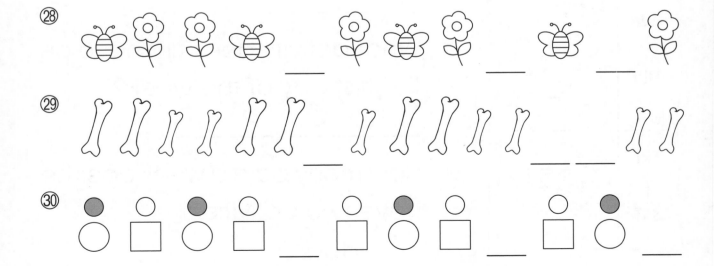

㉘

㉙

㉚

ISBN: 978-1-897164-29-7

Colour the graph. Then fill in the blanks.

Food Item	Cupcake	Doughnut	Croissant	Danish	Cookie
No. of Boxes Sold	卌 ||	||||	卌 |||	卌 ||	卌 ||||

㉛ **Food Sold at Fundraising Fair**

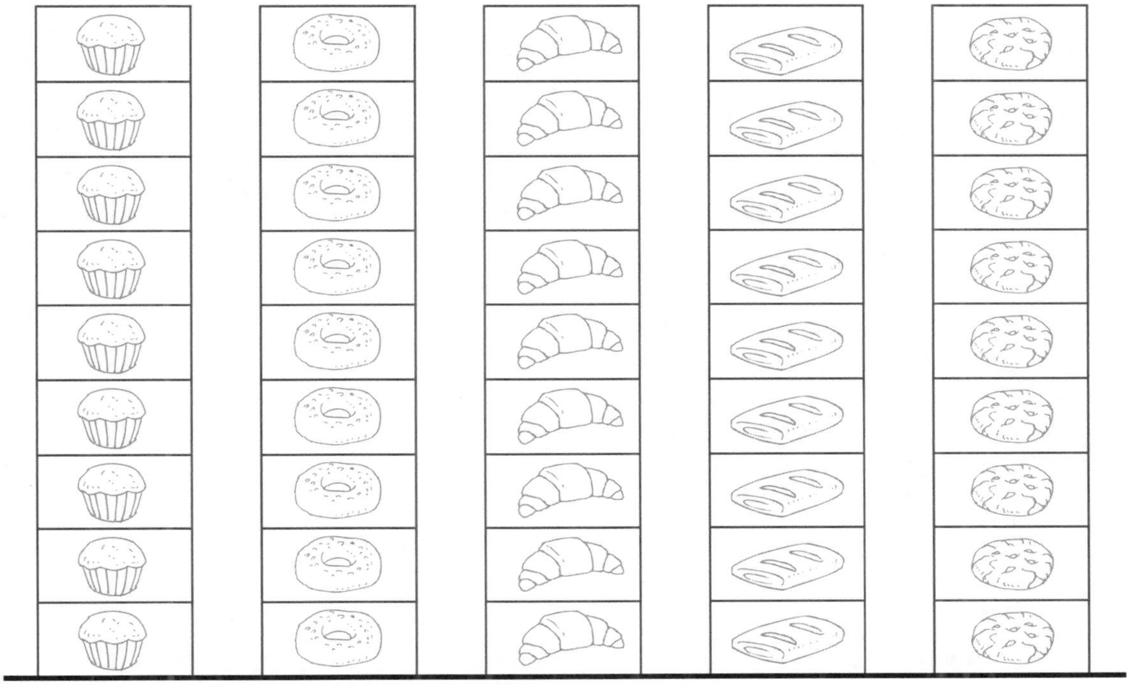

㉜ There were ____________ kinds of food.

㉝ ____________ were sold the most.

㉞ ____________ boxes of food were sold in all.

Use "impossible", "unlikely", "likely", or "certain" to describe the chances.

㉟ *Mrs. Green buys a box of doughnuts. When she opens the box, she will see some cookies there.*

____

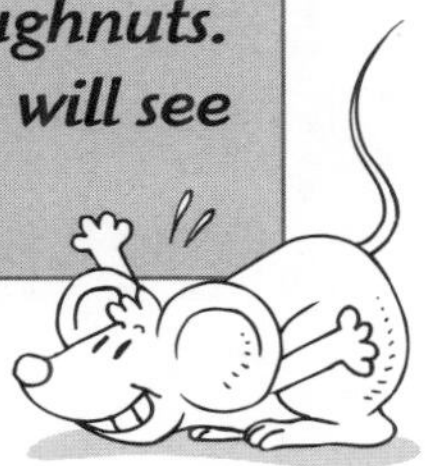

㊱ *Lucy buys a box of 12 cookies. She will finish the cookies with 3 friends tomorrow.*

____

ISBN: 978-1-897164-29-7

ISBN: 978-1-897164-29-7

ISBN: 978-1-897164-29-7

A Visit to a
Petting Farm

Today my class visited a petting farm in the countryside. We saw many animals at the farm. There were goats and pigs. They were fun to watch.

We also watched the farmer milk his cow. He let us try, but it was not easy.

There were some ponies too. We all had a chance to ride. My pony's name was Blaze. It was a lot of fun.

There was a strawberry patch at the petting farm. We all picked some strawberries and ate them after lunch. They tasted so sweet!

I had a great day at the petting farm.

ISBN: 978-1-897164-29-7

A. Complete the sentences with the correct words.

milk   patch   countryside   sweet   animals   ponies

1. The petting farm is in the _____ .

2. The _____ on the farm were fun to watch.

3. The farmer let us _____ the cow.

4. We also rode on _____ .

5. We picked strawberries on a _____ .

6. The strawberries were _____ .

B. Circle ◯ the words in (A) in the word search.

b	h	k	l	e	n	q	i	a	o	u	m	d
p	a	n	i	m	a	l	s	v	l	p	i	c
d	i	s	n	w	z	p	y	g	x	o	l	q
k	c	z	b	j	v	a	h	o	w	n	k	m
g	t	c	o	u	n	t	r	y	s	i	d	e
n	p	m	g	y	j	c	w	e	r	e	i	k
f	a	r	o	u	x	h	l	j	p	s	t	h
e	h	i	c	s	w	e	e	t	d	m	b	f

ISBN: 978-1-897164-29-7

Beginning Consonants

The **beginning consonant** of a word is the beginning sound that is not a vowel (a, e, i, o, u).

Examples: <u>f</u>un   <u>r</u>ide   <u>d</u>ay

C. Say the thing in each picture. Colour the correct beginning consonant.

1.

p
b

2.

s
f

3.

z
s

4.

m
b

5.

f
w

6.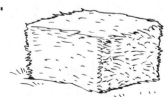

h
k

ISBN: 978-1-897164-29-7

D. **Look at the pictures. Help the boy fill in the beginning consonants of the farm animals.**

You are a...

1.

__oat

2.

__uck

3.

__unny

4.

__ow

5.

__urkey

6.

__ony

7.

__ooster

8.

__ig

ISBN: 978-1-897164-29-7

It is fun to travel on water. Look at the different kinds of boats below.

Canoe – This is a small, long boat. It was first made by the First Nations people. It was made of animal skin or tree bark. Now it is made of fibreglass.

Kayak – This small boat was first made by Canada's northern native people from sealskin. Kayaking is a popular sport now.

Sailboat – A sailboat has large sails, or masts. It moves when the wind blows.

Ocean liner – This is a large ship that carries people across the oceans and seas. These people are on holiday. There are swimming pools, shops, restaurants, and even movie theatres on ocean liners.

Over the Ocean Blue

ISBN: 978-1-897164-29-7

A. Unscramble the letters and write the names of the boats.

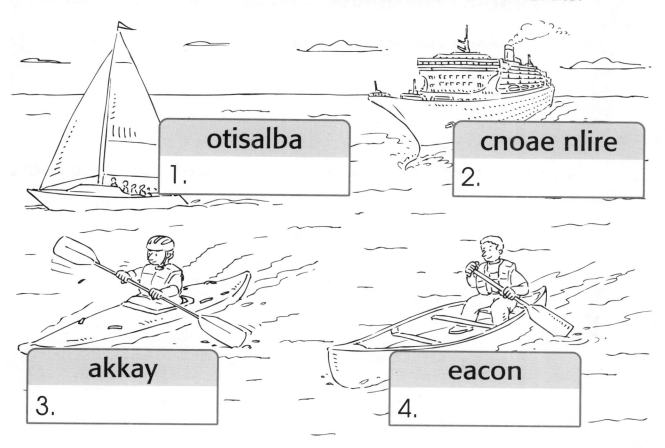

otisalba

1.

cnoae nlire

2.

akkay

3.

eacon

4.

B. Check ✔ the things you can find on an ocean liner.

1.

2.

3.

4.

5.

6.

ISBN: 978-1-897164-29-7

Ending Consonants

The **ending consonant** of a word is the ending sound that is not a vowel.

Examples: trave<u>l</u>   ski<u>n</u>   shi<u>p</u>

C. Colour the pictures in each group that end with the sound of the letter.

1.

l

2.

t

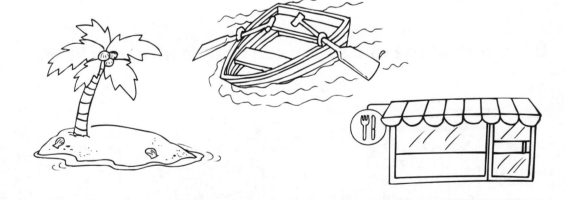

3.

s

ISBN: 978-1-897164-29-7

D. **Draw a line from each letter to the picture that ends with the sound of that letter.**

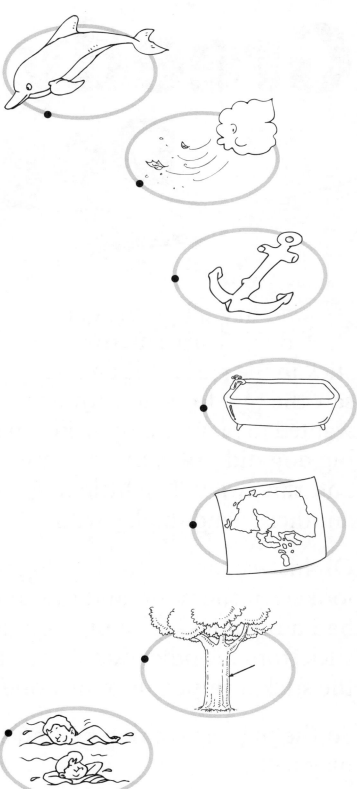

b ·

d ·

k ·

m ·

n ·

p ·

r ·

The Story of the Greedy Dog

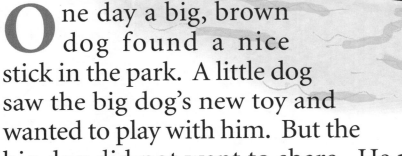

One day a big, brown dog found a nice stick in the park. A little dog saw the big dog's new toy and wanted to play with him. But the big dog did not want to share. He picked up his new toy and ran away. The little dog was sad, but soon he found another friend to play with.

On his way home, the big dog walked next to a pond. He looked in the pond and saw another dog! That dog also had a big stick. The big dog decided he would take the stick from the other dog. When he opened his mouth wide, the stick dropped into the pond!

So the big, brown dog had no stick – and no friends – to play with.

ISBN: 978-1-897164-29-7

A. Find words from the story that mean the opposite of these words.

1 happy

2 narrow

3 old

4 closed

5 small

6 give

B. Circle ◯ "Yes" if the sentences are true. Circle ◯ "No" if they are not true.

1. The big, brown dog found a steak in the park.

Yes / No

2. The big dog did not want to play with the small dog.

Yes / No

3. The little dog played with another friend.

Yes / No

4. The big dog saw another dog swimming in the pond.

Yes / No

5. The big dog dropped his stick into the pond.

Yes / No

ISBN: 978-1-897164-29-7

Short Vowels

Some words with the letters a, e, i, o, or u have the **short vowel sounds**.

Examples: s<u>a</u>d   b<u>i</u>g   p<u>o</u>nd

C. Say the things in the picture. Fill in the missing short vowels.

s n

l mp

m tt

d ll

b x

st ck

p ppy

dr ss

b ll

r g

s ck

ISBN: 978-1-897164-29-7

D. Put a line through the words that have short vowel sounds. Write them on the lines.

The words may go in any directions.

1.

k	g	h
~~s~~	~~a~~	~~d~~
t	a	p

_____sad_____

_____

_____

2.

p	e	t
t	e	q
j	b	n

_____

_____

_____

3.

b	h	l
i	i	t
g	m	b

_____

_____

_____

4.

f	d	b
m	o	p
y	g	x

_____

_____

_____

5.

c	m	s
g	u	b
n	w	p

_____

_____

_____

6.

h	u	t
m	i	k
b	a	g

_____

_____

_____

ISBN: 978-1-897164-29-7

Sometimes We Just Like to Look at the Sky...

Sometimes, on a nice day, my friend and I like to lie down on the grass and look up at the big, blue sky. We can see birds and airplanes and clouds.

Some clouds are soft and fluffy. Some are thin and wispy. Some clouds float away on the wind. Some clouds grow big right in front of our eyes.

We think we can see sailing ships and whales. We close our eyes. When we open them, those ships and whales are gone! Then we see some kittens. We watch the kittens run away. This is fun.

ISBN: 978-1-897164-29-7

A. Colour the  if the sentences are true.

1. The writer likes to look at the sky alone.

2. There are birds and airplanes in the sky.

3. Clouds can be soft and fluffy.

4. Whales swim in the sky.

5. Some clouds look like kittens.

6. It is fun looking at the clouds.

B. What do you see in the sky? Draw a picture to show what you see. Then write a sentence to go with it.

ISBN: 978-1-897164-29-7

Long Vowels

Some words with the letters a, i, o, or u have the **long vowel sounds**. They sound the same as the way you say the letters.

Examples: c<u>a</u>ke   h<u>i</u>de   cl<u>o</u>se   c<u>u</u>be

C. Complete all the words on each kite with the same long vowel. Say the words.

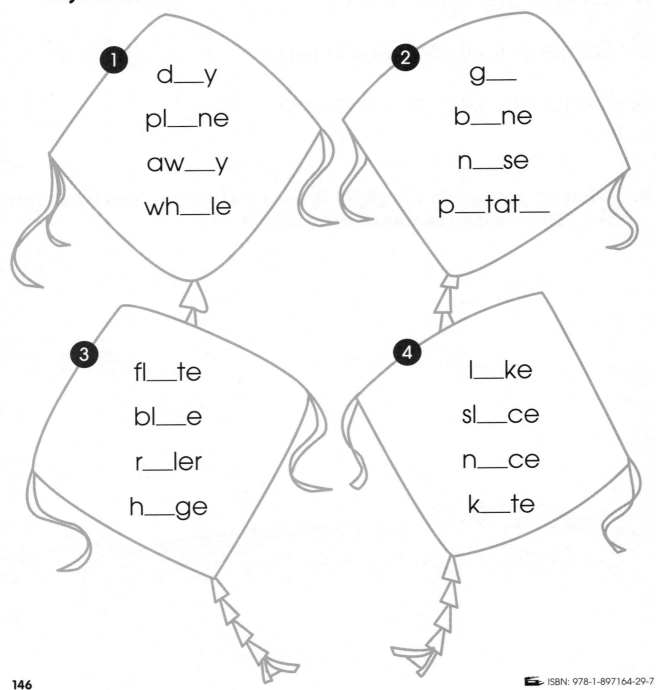

1
d__y
pl__ne
aw__y
wh__le

2
g__
b__ne
n__se
p__tat__

3
fl__te
bl__e
r__ler
h__ge

4
l__ke
sl__ce
n__ce
k__te

ISBN: 978-1-897164-29-7

D. Say the picture clues. Complete the crossword puzzle.

The letter beside each picture tells you the long vowel that the word has.

Variety
– *the* Spice of Life

Salty! Spicy! Sour! Sweet!
I love all the food I eat.
Chicken curry! A red beet stew!
Cucumber sushi! Dim sum, too!

I will give all foods a try
From jambalaya to apple pie.
Healthy food from all sorts of places
Makes healthy bodies and smiling faces.

What's for dinner? I can't wait
For a world of variety on my plate.

ISBN: 978-1-897164-29-7

A. Put the words in the correct boxes.

sushi   sour   salty   dim sum

stew   sweet   apple pie   spicy

Food

_____

_____

_____

_____

Taste

_____

_____

_____

_____

B. Complete the table with words from the rhyme.

1-syllable word	food	
2-syllable word	healthy	
3-syllable word		
4-syllable word	variety	

ISBN: 978-1-897164-29-7

Rhyming Words

Rhyming words are words that have the same ending sound.

Examples: s<u>our</u>   fl<u>ower</u>

C. Draw lines to match the rhyming words.

1. pie •   • stew

2. faces •   • try

3. food •   • spinner

4. dinner •   • eat

5. sweet •   • places

6. curry •   • hurry

7. wait •   • mood

8. too •   • plate

ISBN: 978-1-897164-29-7

D. Look at each picture. Say what it is. Colour the word that rhymes with it.

1.

| teacher | thicken | kicking |

2.

| bushy | sea | sit |

3.

| deer | meat | pear |

4.

| handle | smile | cake |

5.

| stool | moon | good |

6.

| bees | seeds | wheels |

ISBN: 978-1-897164-29-7

A Chant from Ghana

Ghana is a country in West Africa. Children there love "do-this" chants. A leader says the line first, and everyone else repeats it. This is how it sounds.

chay chay koo lay
chay chay koh feen sah
koh fee sah lahn gah
kay tay chee lahn gah
koom ah dayn day
koom ah dayn day
Hey!

As everyone is chanting, they also do actions. This is what the chant means in English:

Hands on your head.
Hands on your shoulders.
Hands on your waist.
Hands on your knees.
Hands on your ankles.
Hands on your ankles.
Hey!

ISBN: 978-1-897164-29-7

A. Put the actions in order. Write 1 to 5.

B. Write two more lines for the chant. Draw the actions for the lines.

Hands on your _____ .

_____

_____

ISBN: 978-1-897164-29-7

Nouns

A **noun** is a word that names an animal, a person, a place, or a thing.

Examples: bear   man   country   hand

C. **Find the nouns. Colour them with your favourite colour.**

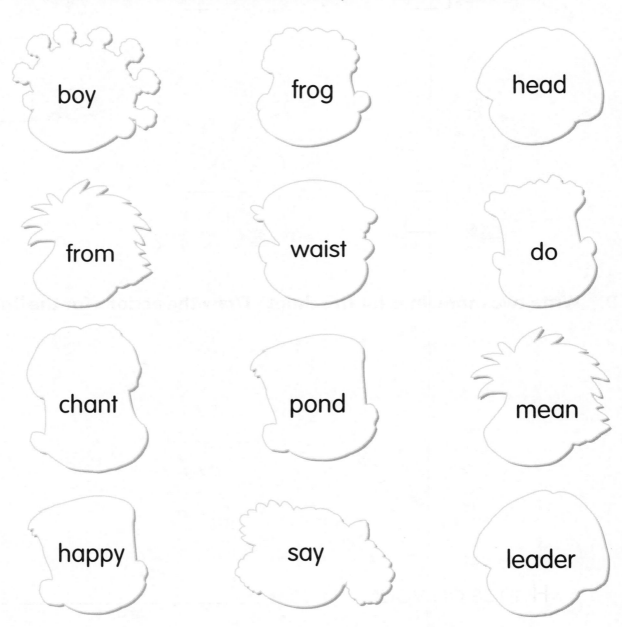

boy   frog   head

from   waist   do

chant   pond   mean

happy   say   leader

ISBN: 978-1-897164-29-7

D. Circle ◯ the nouns in the sentences.

1. A girl is sitting by the pool.

2. Some fish are swimming in the water.

3. The weather is nice.

4. The sun shines brightly in the sky.

5. The children go to the schoolyard.

E. Draw the pictures. Write what they are.

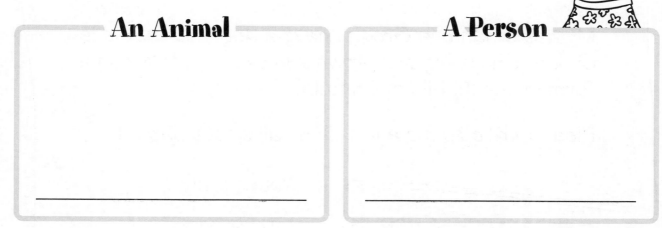

An Animal

_____

A Person

_____

A Place

_____

A Thing

_____

ISBN: 978-1-897164-29-7

A Letter to a New Friend

Dear Kiyoka,

Hello. My name is Sammy. My cousin Miss Wilson gave me your name and address. She is the English teacher at your school. She asked me to be your pen pal. I am glad to have a friend in Japan!

Sammy is my nickname. It is the short name for Samantha. I am seven years old. I have a brother named Hugh. He is ten. My mom's name is Mandy. My dad's name is Greg. I have a dog. Her name is Choco. She is big and brown and sweet. We live on a farm in the middle of Canada.

Please write to me and tell me all about Japan!

Yours truly,

Sammy

P.S. This is a picture of me, my friend Emi, and Choco. Emi is wearing a cap.

ISBN: 978-1-897164-29-7

A. Put the names in ABC order.

Kiyoka
Sammy
Hugh
Mandy
Greg
Choco
Emi

1. _____

2. _____

3. _____

4. _____

5. _____

6. _____

7. _____

B. Circle ◯ the correct words to complete the sentences.

1. This is a letter from ___ .

   Kiyoka   Sammy   Miss Wilson

2. Miss Wilson lives in ___ .

   England   Japan   Canada

3. Sammy wants to be the ___ of Kiyoka.

   cousin   teacher   pen pal

4. Sammy is the nickname of ___ .

   Greg   Hugh   Samantha

5. Sammy's friend is called ___ .

   Mandy   Choco   Emi

ISBN: 978-1-897164-29-7

Common Nouns

A **common noun** names any person, animal, place, or thing.

Examples: sister   duck   garden   paper

C. Help Mr. Postman deliver Sammy's letter to Kiyoka's home by colouring the houses with common nouns.

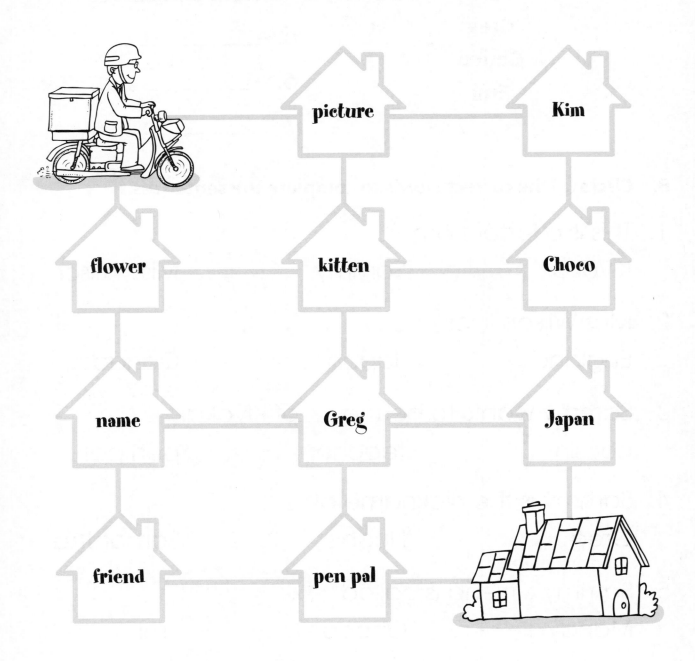

picture   Kim

flower   kitten   Choco

name   Greg   Japan

friend   pen pal

ISBN: 978-1-897164-29-7

D. Put the common nouns in the correct ✉.

Person

_____

_____

_____

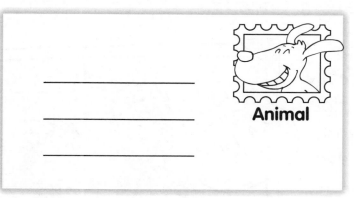

Animal

_____

_____

_____

brother	letter
cousin	dog
school	farm
teacher	bird
horse	park
picture	cap

Place

_____

_____

_____

Thing

_____

_____

_____

ISBN: 978-1-897164-29-7

A Letter from Japan

Dear Sammy,

Thank you for your letter. I was very happy to get it from your cousin. Miss Wilson is a good English teacher. She likes to tell us about Canada.

I live in the middle of Japan. It is a very pretty place. People grow rice and fruit here. I am eight years old. I have a sister. Her name is Keiko and she is six. My mother's name is Hana and my father's name is Kenichi. He works in the  city. He goes there by train every day. My grandfather and grandmother live with us.

This is a photo of me, my sister, and our cat Pekko. This is how you spell your name in Japanese. Please write back soon!

Your friend,

Kiyoka Nakano

ISBN: 978-1-897164-29-7

A. Look at the photo of Kiyoka's family. Write the names in the boxes.

Kiyoka   Keiko   Hana   Kenichi   Pekko

1.

2.

3.

4.

5.

B. Check ✔ if the sentences are true.

1. Miss Wilson is Sammy's English teacher. ____

2. Kiyoka lives in Japan. ____

3. Kiyoka's father works on a train. ____

4. Keiko is Kiyoka's sister. ____

5. There are rice fields near Kiyoka's home. ____

ISBN: 978-1-897164-29-7

Proper Nouns

A **proper noun** names a specific person, animal, place, or thing.
It begins with a capital letter.

Examples: Martha   Nemo   Toronto   Big Mac

C.   Circle ◯ the proper nouns in the sentences.

1. Sammy lives in Canada.

2. Miss Wilson teaches Kiyoka English.

3. People grow rice in the middle of Japan.

4. Can you write your name in Japanese?

5. The Lion King is an interesting story.

6. It is about a lion named Simba.

7. I go to Lakeside School.

8. Toronto is a big city.

9. The girl has a fat cat.
    She calls it Pekko.

ISBN: 978-1-897164-29-7

D. **Replace the underlined words with proper nouns. Write the sentences on the lines.**

Don't forget to begin the proper nouns with capital letters.

1. <u>My friend</u> likes playing with me.

   _____

2. I feed <u>my dog</u> every morning.

   _____

3. My cousin works in <u>a small town</u>.

   _____

4. He is reading <u>a storybook</u>.

   _____

5. <u>She</u> is the best teacher in my school.

   _____

6. <u>The capital city</u> is a nice place to visit.

   _____

ISBN: 978-1-897164-29-7

Our Chores

In our family, everyone helps out around the house.

Every morning, before we go to school, my sister and I make our beds. Then we come downstairs for breakfast. When we finish eating, we carry our dishes to the kitchen sink. Then I fill up our dog Jack's bowls with food and water.

Each evening, after dinner, my sister and I take turns to walk Jack with Mom or Dad.

My sister waters the plants. But I am taller than she is, so I have to water the ones on the shelf.

We like keeping our house clean and tidy.

ISBN: 978-1-897164-29-7

A.   Put the pictures in order.   Write 1 to 6 in the boxes.

B.   Draw a picture to show how you help at home.   Write a sentence to go with it.

Singular and Plural Nouns

A **singular noun** names one person, animal, place, or thing.

Examples: student   bird   pond   pen

A **plural noun** names more than one. Many plural nouns are formed by adding "s" to the singular nouns.

Examples: students   birds   ponds   pens

C. Look at the pictures. Circle ◯ the correct words.

1.

bed

beds

2.

flower

flowers

3.

school

schools

4.

plant

plants

5.

house

houses

6.

mug

mugs

7.

bowl

bowls

8.

book

books

9.

parent

parents

ISBN: 978-1-897164-29-7

D. Look at the picture. Write the words in the boxes. Add "s" to form the plural where needed.

apple   ball   boy
cat   cup   mop
plate   sink   towel

1.

2.

3.

4.

5.

6.

7.

8.

9.

ISBN: 978-1-897164-29-7

Mr. Mom

Did you know the "daddy" emperor penguin has a very important job?

When the female penguin lays an egg, she will give it to the father penguin. The egg rests on the father penguin's flippers, and a fold of furry skin on his belly keeps the egg warm. The father takes care of the egg and the mother goes to the sea to eat!

The mother penguin returns about two months later. Her stomach is full of food that she will give to her baby. After the baby is born, the mother penguin will take care of it. Now it is daddy's turn to go back to the sea to find food. He is hungry!

ISBN: 978-1-897164-29-7

A. Put the sentences in order. Write 1 to 5 on the eggs.

◯ The mother penguin gives the egg to the father penguin.

◯ The mother penguin lays an egg.

◯ The father penguin goes to find food.

◯ The mother penguin goes to find food in the sea.

◯ The mother penguin returns with food for the baby.

B. What do you think the emperor penguin eats? Draw a picture of an emperor penguin finding food in the sea. Fill in the blank to complete the sentence.

The emperor penguin eats _____ .

ISBN: 978-1-897164-29-7

Sentences

A **sentence** is a group of words that tells a complete thought about someone or something. It begins with a capital letter and ends with a period (.).

Example: The baby is born.

C. **Colour the**  **if the group of words forms a sentence.**

1. In this world.

2. The emperor penguins are cute.

3. The father takes care of.

4. and find food.

5. Penguins have flippers.

6. She gives the food to the baby.

7. They are very hungry.

8. Two months later.

9. The father returns.

ISBN: 978-1-897164-29-7

D. Match the groups of words to form sentences. Write the letters.

1. Kelly likes   _____   **A** picture.

2. She is drawing   _____   **B** a big egg.

3. A baby penguin   _____   **C** drawing.

4. The penguin is   _____   **D** cute.

5. I love her   _____   **E** is coming out of it.

E. Look at the picture. Write two sentences about it.

1. _____

2. _____

ISBN: 978-1-897164-29-7

Perogies

Many Canadians love perogies. A perogy is like a dumpling. You fill a pocket of dough with a mixture of mashed potatoes and cheese. You can eat them boiled or fried. They taste great with fried onions and melted butter, and some sour cream.

You can make perogies in other flavours, too. Some people put sour cabbage in their perogies. Others like to put fruit inside, such as bits of plum or peach.

ISBN: 978-1-897164-29-7

A. Colour the things for making and eating perogies.

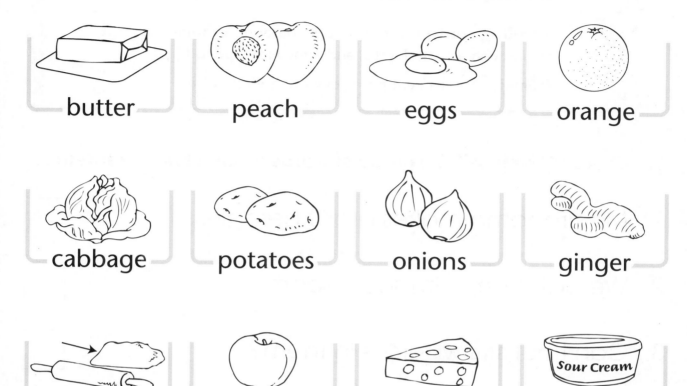

butter	peach	eggs	orange
cabbage	potatoes	onions	ginger
dough	plum	cheese	sour cream

B. Replace the underlined words with words from the passage.

1. <u>A lot of</u> people eat perogies with fried onions. _____

2. They <u>stuff</u> the Christmas stocking with small toys. _____

3. We all <u>enjoy</u> tacos. _____

4. This ice cream is <u>really nice</u>. _____

ISBN: 978-1-897164-29-7

Telling Sentences

A **telling sentence** tells about someone or something. It begins with a capital letter and ends with a period (.).

Example: You can eat perogies with melted butter.

C. Check ✔ the box if the group of words forms a telling sentence.

1. My grandma makes great perogies. ☐

2. We eat them with sour cream. ☐

3. Can I put strawberries in them? ☐

4. I love them fried. ☐

5. Wow, yummy! ☐

6. Could I have some more? ☐

ISBN: 978-1-897164-29-7

D. Write the telling sentences correctly.

1. i like perogies

   _____

2. tony loves toast with jam

   _____

3. ice cream is kim's favourite

   _____

4. we all enjoy eating

   _____

E. Draw your favourite food. Write a sentence about it.

My Favourite Food

_____

_____

The Sun and the Wind

One day the sun and the wind were watching a man walk in the park. He was wearing a big, heavy coat.

"I'm so strong," said the wind. "I can make that coat come off the man."

The sun smiled. "Go ahead, show me," said the sun.

The wind began to blow. It blew and blew. It was so hard for the man to walk in the wind! But the wind could not blow the coat off the man's body.

"Watch me," said the sun.

The sun shone bright and hot. Soon the man stopped walking. He wiped his forehead with his handkerchief. Then he took off his coat!

ISBN: 978-1-897164-29-7

A. Help the wind blow the wrong letters away from the misspelled words. Cross out ✗ the letters and write the correct spellings on the lines.

1.

   _____

2.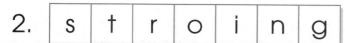

   _____

3.

   _____

4.

   _____

5. | f | p | o | r | e | h | e | a | d |

   _____

B. Circle ◯ the correct words to complete the sentences.

1. The man was in the ___ .

   park   school   backyard

2. The man was wearing a ___ .

   thin coat   heavy jumper   heavy coat

3. It was ___ to walk in the wind.

   easy   hard   fun

4. The man wiped his forehead with his ___ .

   coat   hand   handkerchief

ISBN: 978-1-897164-29-7

Asking Sentences

An **asking sentence** asks about someone or something. It begins with a capital letter and ends with a question mark (?).

Example: What do you like?

C. Check ✔ "Yes" for asking sentences. Check ✔ "No" for those that are not.

<table>
<tr><td></td><td>**Yes**</td><td>**No**</td></tr>
<tr><td>1. Let's play a game.</td><td>☐</td><td>☐</td></tr>
<tr><td>2. Can you make him take off his coat?</td><td>☐</td><td>☐</td></tr>
<tr><td>3. Is the wind strong?</td><td>☐</td><td>☐</td></tr>
<tr><td>4. What a hot day!</td><td>☐</td><td>☐</td></tr>
<tr><td>5. How can you do that?</td><td>☐</td><td>☐</td></tr>
<tr><td>6. I will surely win next time.</td><td>☐</td><td>☐</td></tr>
<tr><td>7. Can I join you?</td><td>☐</td><td>☐</td></tr>
</table>

ISBN: 978-1-897164-29-7

D. Draw lines to match the two parts to form asking sentences.

1. Is

2. Do

3. Why

4. Who

5. What

6. When

- can we do in winter?

- is the winter so long?

- will the snow stop?

- likes snowy days?

- it cold in the fall?

- you like fluffy snow?

E. Write the asking sentences correctly.

1. is it windy outside

_____

2. do you have a thicker coat

_____

3. where are you going

_____

4. are you coming with me

_____

Duck Hunting
A Story from China

One day, two duck hunters went out to hunt some ducks. Soon, a big duck came by. Both men wanted to catch the duck. The duck flew closer and closer.

"That duck will be very good in our soup," said the first man. "I love soup."

"No," said the other man. "When I catch this duck, I will roast it. A good roast duck is better than soup."

"I don't think so. I like duck soup the most," said the first man.

"But I love roast duck," said the other hunter.

"Soup!"

"Roast!"

The two hunters started to yell at each other, and the big duck flew away.

ISBN: 978-1-897164-29-7

A. Check ✔ the correct sentence in each pair.

1. The hunters wanted to hunt some ducks.　A

   The hunters wanted to save some ducks.　B

2. The duck loved soup.　A

   The first hunter loved soup.　B

3. The other hunter would roast the duck.　A

   The other hunter would fry the duck.　B

4. The hunters yelled at each other.　A

   The hunters yelled at the duck.　B

5. At last, the duck swam away.　A

   At last, the duck flew away.　B

B. Write what you think the duck is saying.

ISBN: 978-1-897164-29-7

13

Surprising Sentences

A **surprising sentence** shows strong feelings like fear, anger, and excitement. It begins with a capital letter and ends with an exclamation mark (!).

Example: What an interesting story!

C. Colour the 🦆 for surprising sentences.

1. There is a duck in the sky.

2. Wow, that duck is big!

3. Can you catch it?

4. I will make duck soup with it.

5. Nice soup!

6. Yuck! I hate duck soup!

7. Oh no, it's gone!

8. How lucky the duck is!

182

ISBN: 978-1-897164-29-7

D. **You are playing a duck hunting game. What will you say when you miss a duck? Check ✔ the correct box.**

Great!

Bad luck!

GAME OVER

HOME

E. **Write the surprising sentences correctly.**

1. what a narrow escape

_____

2. dear me

_____

3. you won't believe it

_____

4. how bad the hunters are

_____

I Like Winter

In Canada we have four seasons: winter, spring, summer, and fall. Some people don't like winter. They think it is too cold. But I love winter! I wrote a poem about it:

My Favourite Season

Winter spring summer fall
I like winter best of all.
The air is cold,
The sun shines bright.
I love to play
In snow so white.

Did you know that some countries have only two seasons: a wet season and a dry season?

ISBN: 978-1-897164-29-7

A.   Look at the pictures. Write the four seasons.

1.

_____

2.

_____

3.

_____

4.

_____

B.   Complete the poem in your own words.

My Favourite Season

Winter spring summer fall

I like _____ best of all.

_____

_____

I love to _____

_____

ISBN: 978-1-897164-29-7

Using Capital Letters (1)

Always begin a sentence with a **capital letter**. Use capital letters for proper nouns and the pronoun "I".

Example: <u>M</u>y sister and <u>I</u> will meet <u>N</u>ancy tomorrow.

C. **Underline the proper nouns in the sentences. Write them correctly on the lines.**

1. There are four seasons in canada. _____

2. The algonquin park looks great in the fall. _____

3. kathleen is going camping this summer. _____

4. Will albert join her? _____

5. Let's go to ottawa in spring. _____

6. Are we staying at windsor hotel? _____

7. We'll take our dog, oscar, with us. _____

ISBN: 978-1-897164-29-7

D. Check ✔ the correct sentences. Cross ✗ and rewrite the wrong ones.

There are only two correct sentences.

1. my sister and i like playing in snow.

    _____

2. We build big snowmen every winter.

    _____

3. cindy names every snowman we build.

    _____

4. The biggest one is called starlie.

    _____

5. i like witty, the smallest one, best.

    _____

6. Which one do you like?

    _____

ISBN: 978-1-897164-29-7

A. Aedo the Alien and Roboguide are visiting the Earth. Help them write the beginning consonants of what they see in the ☐ and the ending consonants in the ☐.

ISBN: 978-1-897164-29-7

B. **Roboguide is teaching Aedo to say the things in English. Help Aedo fill in the missing vowels. Then say them aloud to Aedo.**

Some words with the letters a, e, i, o, or u have the short vowel sounds. Others have the long vowel sounds. Long vowel sounds sound the same as the way you say the letters.

1.

t__p

2.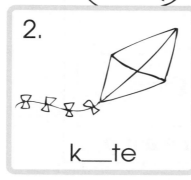

k__te

3.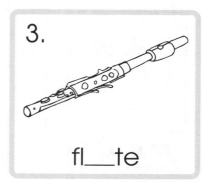

fl__te

4.

fr__me

5.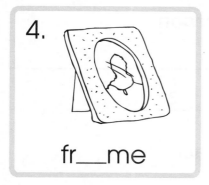

y__-y__

6.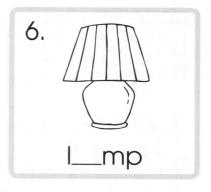

l__mp

7.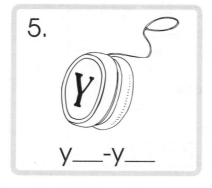

t__nt

8.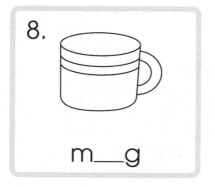

m__g

9.

f__sh

ISBN: 978-1-897164-29-7

C. Aedo has taken some pictures. Help Roboguide unscramble the letters to write the nouns in the correct groups.

a b b y

a b c e h

m o o t t a

l e a n p

i r v r e d

p o p h i

g r f o

a p k r

A noun names an animal, a person, a place, or a thing.

Animal

_____

_____

Person

_____

_____

Place

_____

_____

Thing

_____

_____

ISBN: 978-1-897164-29-7

D. Aedo and Roboguide are reading a poster. Help them circle ○ the common nouns and underline the proper nouns.

Blue Hedge Company

Final sale this Saturday and Sunday
Everything must go!

D&Y tableware

(dinner plates, cups and saucers, and salad bowls only)

Video games

GAME GAME

Storybooks by Karen Wilson

The Angel's Heart

Why Anna Valued Every Summer

All stationery

I-Time clocks

A common noun names any person, animal, place, or thing. A proper noun names a specific person, animal, place, or thing. It begins with a capital letter.

E. Write what Aedo is going to buy.

I want to buy 1 ☕ , 3 📖 , 1 ⏰ , and 5 ✏️ for my friends.

Things Aedo is going to buy:

one _____

_____

ISBN: 978-1-897164-29-7

F. Aedo is talking to Roboguide in English. Colour the if the groups of words form sentences.

1. What can I.

2. Busy city.

3. The Earth is beautiful.

4. It's a pity we can't stay here longer.

5. Let's pay a visit to Mars.

6. That deer over there.

7. The bear is stronger.

8. A dot on it.

G. Find six pairs of rhyming words from what Aedo says above.

1. _____ ; _____   2. _____ ; _____

3. _____ ; _____   4. _____ ; _____

5. _____ ; _____   6. _____ ; _____

   ISBN: 978-1-897164-29-7

H. Aedo is about to leave the Earth. Add the correct punctuation marks at the end of the sentences. Then write what types of sentences they are.

A telling sentence tells about something. An asking sentence asks about something. A surprising sentence shows strong feelings.

"T" for telling sentences
"A" for asking sentences
"S" for surprising sentences

1. How do you find this trip ☐

2. Wow, it's great ☐

3. Which part do you like best ☐

4. I like going shopping best ☐

5. What's your next stop ☐

6. I'm visiting Mars ☐

7. What a wonderful plan ☐

8. It's time to leave now ☐

9. How sad ☐

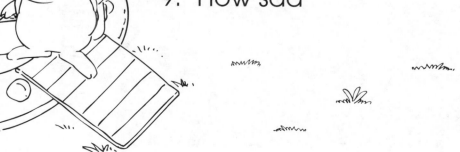

ISBN: 978-1-897164-29-7

The Storybook Club

My friends and I have a storybook club. Each Saturday morning, we meet at someone's house to read storybooks together. We each bring one storybook and then take turns reading our story to everyone else.

Once a month, one of our mothers takes us all to the library. We love going there! Sometimes there is an author at the library, and he or she reads stories to us. Sometimes the librarian reads stories. After storytime, we look at the books on the shelves. My friends and I each choose three books to take home.

I like our storybook club very much.

ISBN: 978-1-897164-29-7

A. Colour the 📖 for the things the children do at the storybook club.

1. Take turns to read stories.

2. Write a short story.

3. Borrow others' storybooks home.

4. Go to the library once a month.

5. Read stories to an author.

6. Borrow some books from the library.

B. Draw a cover for your favourite storybook. Write a sentence to tell why you like it.

Using Capital Letters (2)

Days of the week, months of the year, and festivals all begin with **capital letters**.

Examples: <u>S</u>aturday   <u>A</u>ugust   <u>V</u>alentine's <u>D</u>ay

C.   Write the words correctly in the right places on the calendar.

Calendar

mother's day   tuesday   easter

halloween   may   november

thanksgiving   july   sunday

wednesday   monday   march

Day of the Week	Month of the Year	Festival

ISBN: 978-1-897164-29-7

D. Write the sentences correctly.

1. i like christmas.

    _____

2. it is on december 25.

    _____

    _____

3. it is a thursday this year.

    _____

4. we are holding a party on christmas day.

    _____

    _____

5. i will invite my friend sandra to come.

    _____

    _____

6. i will give her an invitation card this friday.

    _____

    _____

ISBN: 978-1-897164-29-7

Snow Day

Dear Kiyoka,

There was a big snowstorm last night. When I woke up this morning, there were piles of snow everywhere! My mother turned on the radio, and it said that schools were closed! My mother is a teacher, so she stayed at home with me and Choco.

This is a list of all the things we did today:

Build a snowman.
Play with Choco.
Make chocolate chip cookies (my dad's favourite).
Phone my grandparents.
Write to you!

I like snow days, but I will be happy to go back to school tomorrow.

Your friend,

Sammy

P.S. Do you have snow days in Japan?

ISBN: 978-1-897164-29-7

A. Check ✔ what Sammy did.

B. What will you do on a snow day? Draw a picture and write a sentence to go with it.

ISBN: 978-1-897164-29-7

Punctuation (1)

All sentences end with **punctuation marks**.

· A telling sentence ends with a period (.).
· An asking sentence ends with a question mark (?).
· A surprising sentence ends with an exclamation mark (!).

C. Complete the sentences with the correct punctuation marks.

1. How are you, Grandma ☐

2. I made muffins with Mom ☐

3. They are yummy ☐

4. You'll like them ☐

5. Is Grandpa home ☐

6. Where is he ☐

7. Will you come over to our place tomorrow ☐

8. Great ☐

9. I will save some muffins for you ☐

ISBN: 978-1-897164-29-7

Punctuation (2)

We use a **comma** (,) to separate items in a list.

Example: I love cookies, muffins, and fruit tarts.

D. Add commas at the correct places in the sentences.

1. Jasmine David and I go swimming every Sunday.

2. I love having toast sausages and milk for breakfast.

3. Pink blue green and purple are my favourite colours.

4. You need to bring glue scissors and some clips to class tomorrow.

5. Put your dolls teddy bears and building blocks back to the toy box.

6. My sister likes eating pancakes with jam honey or maple syrup.

7. Spring summer fall and winter are the four seasons in Canada.

8. Do you want lollipops chocolate or cotton candy?

My Mom, the Student

My mom used to work in a hospital every day. She worked in the kitchen. She cooked healthy meals for the people in the hospital.

My mom liked working at the hospital. She liked seeing sick people get better. She started to think that maybe she could help sick people get better, too.

My mom made a plan. She was going to go back to school!

Now my mom and I are both students. We study hard. My mom still works in the kitchen at the hospital, but not every day. When she finishes her school, my mom will be a nurse.

I am very proud of my mom.

ISBN: 978-1-897164-29-7

A. Circle ◯ the correct words to complete the sentences.

1. The writer's mom worked in the kitchen of __ .

   a school   a hospital   someone's home

2. People in the hospital need to eat __ .

   fast food   junk food   healthy food

3. The writer's mom wants to be a __ .

   nurse   doctor   cook

4. The writer is a __ .

   cook   teacher   student

B. Fill in the blanks with words from the passage.

1. Doctors and nurses help _____ people get better.

2. My grandparents eat five _____ a day.

3. My dad saves many people's lives in fires. I am _____ of him.

4. _____ she'll come. I'm not sure.

5. We have to _____ hard to get good grades.

ISBN: 978-1-897164-29-7

Subjects

The **subject** of a sentence tells whom or what the sentence is about.

Example: The sick <u>people</u> are getting better.

C.   Circle ◯ the subject of each sentence.

1. My mom bakes great food.

2. I like her pastries.

3. The chocolate pastries are best of all.

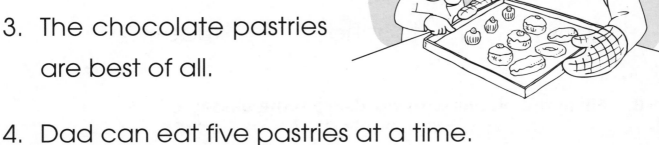

4. Dad can eat five pastries at a time.

5. Our neighbours sometimes come over to learn baking from my mom.

6. Mrs. Wrights can now make yummy tarts.

7. Her sons like having them for breakfast.

8. They ask their mom to bake tarts every day.

   ISBN: 978-1-897164-29-7

D. **Look at the pictures. Complete the sentences with the correct subjects.**

children   brothers   girl   boy   dog

1. The _____ has a cute dog.

2. The two _____ are playing with their toys.

3. The _____ is naughty.

4. The _____ are having fun in the pool.

5. The _____ is enjoying his ice cream cone.

ISBN: 978-1-897164-29-7

The Giant Turnip
A *Story from* Russia

One day, a poor farmer wanted to plant his vegetable garden. He liked turnips, but his wife and children did not. His wife liked peas. His son liked beans. His daughter liked carrots. So they picked straws to find a winner. The farmer won.

The farmer planted a turnip seed. Soon, the turnip began to grow. The farmer watered it every day. It grew and grew.

At the end of summer, it was time to pull the turnip out of the soil. The farmer pulled and pulled. But the turnip was so big, it would not come out. His wife came to help him pull. They pulled and pulled. Their son came to help them, too, but the turnip would not come out.

Then the little girl came out to help. They all pulled and pulled. The giant turnip came out of the ground. The family took the turnip home. They cooked turnip soup. Everyone loved it.

ISBN: 978-1-897164-29-7

A. **Match the people with the vegetables they liked. Write the letters in the boxes.**

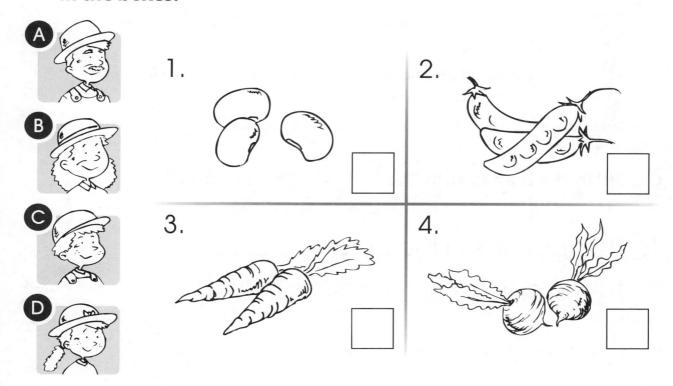

1.

2.

3.

4.

B. **Put the sentences in order. Write 1 to 6 on the turnips.**

The farmer and his wife tried to pull the turnip out.

Their daughter came out to help too.

The farmer and his family picked straws to decide on what to plant.

They made soup with the turnip.

The farmer planted a turnip seed.

Their son came to help.

ISBN: 978-1-897164-29-7

Pronouns

A **pronoun** takes the place of a noun. "He", "she", "it", "they", "I", "you", and "we" are pronouns.

Example: The pumpkins are ready for picking. <u>They</u> make great pumpkin pies.

C. Fill in the blanks with "he", "she", "it", or "they".

1. The farmer is in the garden. _____ is taking care of his plants.

2. He likes planting turnips. _____ sometimes grow very big.

3. His wife is cooking soup in the kitchen. _____ smells good.

4. Their daughter loves carrots. _____ drinks carrot juice every day.

5. The farmer's son likes all kinds of beans. _____ wants to have his own garden of beans.

6. Their dog eats everything. _____ likes watermelons the best!

  ISBN: 978-1-897164-29-7

D. Circle ◯ the correct pronouns to complete the sentences.

1. I   He   want to grow some  in the backyard.

2. I   He   want to give them to 🧑 for her birthday

next year.   3. He   She   likes 🌷, so   4. I   she   am

going to grow 🌷 of different colours.

👴 knows a lot about gardening.   5. I   He   will

go to get some 🌷 bulbs with me.   6. He   She   said

to me, "   7. We   They   will bloom in early spring.

8. We   They   will take

care of the plants

together."

Mr. Music's One-Man Band

Hello! My name is Mr. Music and this is my one-man band!

What can you see on my knees? They are cymbals. I knock my knees together and they go CRASH!

What am I holding in my right hand? It is a drumstick. I hit the kettle drum with the stick to make a big BOOM!

What can you see on my ankles? They are bells. I give my legs a shake and the bells jingle and ring.

What can you see next to my left hand? It's a keyboard. With one hand I can play lovely music.

What can you see in front of my mouth? It is a harmonica. It makes a wonderful sound.

Clap your hands, children. Let's sing and dance!

ISBN: 978-1-897164-29-7

A.   Look at the picture clues.   Complete the crossword puzzle.

B.   Give short answers to the questions.

1.   How many members are there in the band?

_____

2.   What does Mr. Music use to hit his kettle drum?

_____

3.   Where are the bells?

_____

4.   What is in front of Mr. Music's mouth?

_____

ISBN: 978-1-897164-29-7

Verbs

Most **verbs** are action words. They tell the things you do.

Example: We <u>walk</u> to school every day.

C. Colour the if the underlined word in each sentence is an action word.

1. Dad <u>puts</u> a big star at the top of the Christmas tree.

2. Mom places some <u>presents</u> underneath it.

3. We <u>tie</u> some bells to the tree.

4. They jingle when we <u>touch</u> them.

5. My <u>sister</u> plays the keyboard.

6. I hit the <u>drum</u> with drumsticks.

7. We <u>sing</u> Christmas carols together.

8. Our dog <u>dances</u> to the music.

9. We <u>enjoy</u> a great Christmas.

ISBN: 978-1-897164-29-7

D. Look at the picture. Write the action words in the correct boxes.

claps   shakes   gives   plays   holds   strikes

1.

2.

3.

4.

5.

6.

ISBN: 978-1-897164-29-7

My New Dog

"Look at my new pet, Timmy!"

"It is a beautiful dog. Is it an Irish Setter?"

"Yes, you're right! We named him Blaze because he is red like fire."

"Did you get him at a pet shop, Emily?"

"No. My father took me to the dog pound. There were many dogs there. They did not have owners. Some of them looked sad. I chose Blaze. I am happy to have my new dog."

"It is important to care for animals."

"Yes. Having a dog is a lot of work. My parents help me feed him and exercise him every day. Blaze is my best friend."

ISBN: 978-1-897164-29-7

A. Read the questions. Circle ◯ the answers in the word search.

- Who took Emily to get a new pet?
- Where did they get it?
- What is its name?
- What colour is it?
- What is an Irish Setter?
- How does Emily feel to have a new pet?
- How often does Emily exercise her pet?

		d	B	g				
	e	a	n	l	o		c	
B	v	q	h	a	p	p	y	k
k	g	e	d	e	z	v	i	m	d	b
s	a	r	s	r	e	d	u	r	o	h
i	t	y	l	j	h	r	p	i	g	e
v	c		w	B	l	g	m		r	j
m	y	d	o	g		p	o	u	n	d
d	o	a	t	x	f	a	t	h	e	r
f	m	y	p	l	i	q	b	s	d	n

ISBN: 978-1-897164-29-7

Am, Is, and Are (1)

"**Am**", "**is**", and "**are**" tell what someone or something is.

"Am" is used with "I".
"Is" is used to tell about one person, animal, place, or thing.
"Are" is used to tell about more than one person, animal, place, or thing.

Examples: I <u>am</u> a student.
Ginny <u>is</u> my neighbour.
We <u>are</u> good friends.

B. Circle ◯ the correct words to complete the sentences.

1. My dog Snow White am / is / are a Pekingese.

2. She am / is / are white and fluffy.

3. I am / is / are happy to have her as my pet.

4. My sister am / is / are afraid of dogs, but she also thinks that Snow White am / is / are cute.

5. Beef sausages am / is / are Snow White's favourite treats.

ISBN: 978-1-897164-29-7

Am, Is, and Are (2)

"**Am**", "**is**", and "**are**" can be used with the "ing" form of a verb to tell what someone or something is doing.

Examples: I <u>am watering</u> the plants.

The sun <u>is shining</u>.

The flowers <u>are blooming</u>.

C.   Look at the pictures.   Fill in the blanks with "am", "is", or "are".

1.

Meg and Joe _____ exercising their dog.

2.

The children _____ painting.

3.

Kenny the Clown _____ giving out balloons.

4.

I _____ learning ballet.

5.

Porky the Pig _____ playing hide-and-seek with the boy.

ISBN: 978-1-897164-29-7

Starry Starry Night

Uncle Sam is an astronomer. He gets to look at the planets and the stars. Uncle Sam gave me a big telescope for my birthday. On a clear night last week, we looked through the telescope together. I saw a very bright spot in the sky. My uncle told me it was the planet Venus!

Uncle Sam showed me groups of stars that look like pictures. He showed me "The Big Dipper". It looks like a big pot with a long handle. He showed me one called "the Broken W". It looks like a "w", but it is a little bit lopsided.

I love looking at the starry night sky. Maybe I will be an astronomer, too!

ISBN: 978-1-897164-29-7

A. Read the clues and find the words from the story.

1. a container for taking up water   _____

2. The Earth is one.   _____

3. person who studies outer space   _____

4. leaning to one side   _____

5. It makes things far away
   appear larger and closer.   _____

B. Read the story and answer the questions.

1. What is Uncle Sam?

   _____

2. What birthday present did Uncle Sam give the
   writer?

   _____

3. What does "The Big Dipper" look like?

   _____

4. Which group of stars looks like a "w"?

   _____

ISBN: 978-1-897164-29-7

Adjectives (1)

An **adjective** is a word that describes a noun (person, animal, place, or thing). It often tells how someone or something looks.

Example: The <u>twinkling</u> stars are <u>amazing</u>.

C. Draw lines to match the adjectives with the correct pictures.

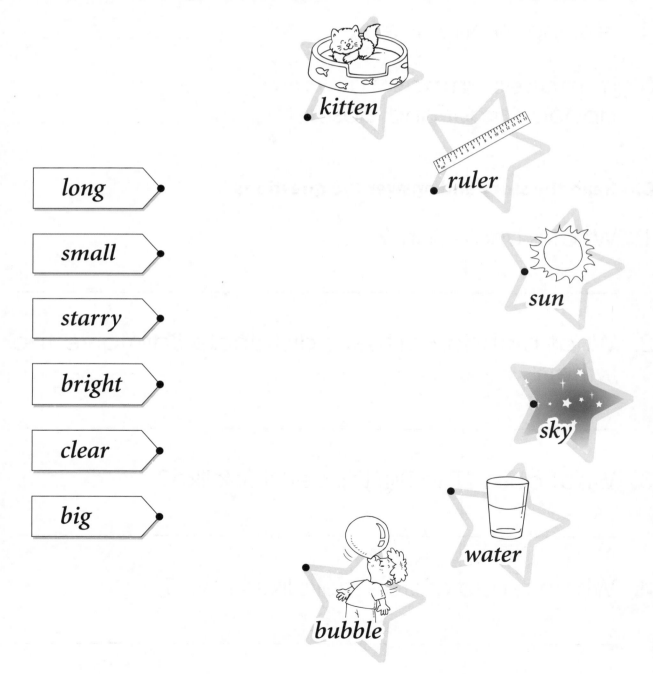

long

small

starry

bright

clear

big

kitten

ruler

sun

sky

water

bubble

ISBN: 978-1-897164-29-7

Adjectives (2)

Some **adjectives** tell about the number or colour of people, animals, places, or things.

Example: The <u>three</u> puppies are <u>black</u> and <u>white</u>.

D. Look at the pictures. Fill in the blanks with numbers and colour the pictures.

1.

_____ brown bees

2.

_____ red butterfly

3.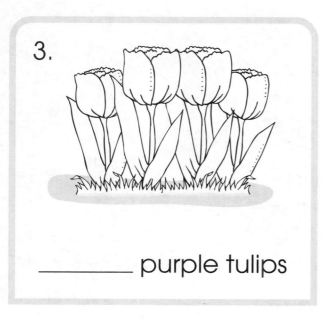

_____ purple tulips

4.

_____ yellow sunflowers

Let's play hide and seek.
Count to ten and I won't peek.
Let's play the game outside
Where you can find a place to hide.

Where can everyone be?
Behind the bushes or up in the tree?
Around the corner or over there?
I can't see anyone anywhere.

But wait. What's that?
I hear a sound.
It's Sam's laughter.
He's been found!

Come out! Come out!
I can see you.
Your dog's wagging his tail
And he gave me the clue.

Hide
and
Seek

ISBN: 978-1-897164-29-7

A. Pair up the words that rhyme. Write them in the trees.

there   sound   clue   be

hide   peek   you   anywhere

seek   outside   tree   found

1

there
anywhere

2

3

4

5

6

B. Fill in the blanks with words from the rhyme.

1. _____ inside. Don't let them find us.

2. _____ one, two, and three and the bunny will be gone!

3. It is fun playing this _____ .

4. My sock was lost but now it is _____ .

5. Why is there no _____ for this puzzle?

ISBN: 978-1-897164-29-7

Location Words

A **location word** shows where someone or something is. "In", "on", "behind", "beside", "over", and "under" are some of the location words.

Example: The park is <u>beside</u> the shopping mall.

C. Fill in the blanks to tell where the animals are.

1.

   dog – _____ the rug

2.

   cat – _____ the table

3.

   fish – _____ the fish bowl

4.

   bunny – _____ the bushes

5.

   bird – _____ the ball

ISBN: 978-1-897164-29-7

D. Read and complete the picture.

- Draw a sun <u>over</u> the house.
- Draw a fountain <u>beside</u> the house.
- Draw six apples <u>in</u> the tree.
- Draw a bike <u>under</u> the tree.
- Draw a cat walking <u>on</u> the path.
- Draw a girl <u>behind</u> the cat.

ISBN: 978-1-897164-29-7

My Wobbly Tooth

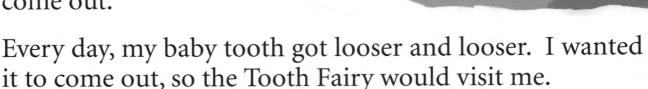

My bottom tooth came out yesterday. It had been wobbly for a long time. My grandpa told me to wobble it with my finger every day, to help it come out.

Every day, my baby tooth got looser and looser. I wanted it to come out, so the Tooth Fairy would visit me.

Yesterday, Grandpa and I had an apple for snack together. When I bit into the apple – guess what – my tooth came out!

I put my tooth under my pillow last night. When I woke up this morning, I found a quarter there!

ISBN: 978-1-897164-29-7

A. Read the story. Circle ◯ the correct word(s) for each sentence.

1. Every day / Yesterday , my bottom tooth came out.

2. I wobbled my tooth with my finger / toe .

3. I wanted Grandpa / the Tooth Fairy to visit me.

4. I had an apple / apple pie for snack.

5. I found my tooth / a quarter under my pillow.

B. Read the clue words. Complete the crossword puzzle with their opposites from the story.

Across

A. here
B. evening
C. short
D. top
E. on

Down

1. lost
2. alone
3. tighter

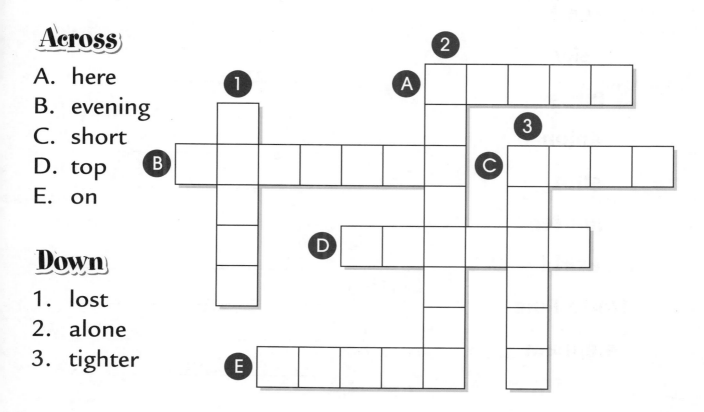

ISBN: 978-1-897164-29-7

Articles

"A", "an", and "the" are **articles**.

"A" is used before a noun that begins with a consonant.
"An" is used before a noun that begins with a vowel.
"The" is used before a noun that names a particular person, animal, place, or thing.

Examples: <u>a</u> box   <u>an</u> orange   <u>the</u> sun

C. Write the nouns in the correct boxes.

Tooth Fairy

apple

oar

tooth

sky

pillow

onion

string

quarter

world

North Pole

elephant

a _____
_____
_____
_____

an _____
_____
_____
_____

the _____
_____
_____
_____

ISBN: 978-1-897164-29-7

D. **Write what the pictures are with "a", "an", or "the" and the correct words.**

owl   dragon   Olympic Games

CN Tower   Easter egg   Earth

1.

_____

2.

_____

3.

_____

4.

_____

5.

_____

6.

_____

ISBN: 978-1-897164-29-7

My Perfect Day

My perfect day would have a lot of my favourite things in it. The singing birds would wake me up, not my alarm clock. Downstairs, my favourite bowl of porridge would be waiting for me. I would wear my favourite blue dress to school. On my way to school, I would find a "lucky charm", maybe a bright, new penny on the sidewalk.

At school, I would play with someone new at recess. I would open my lunch bag at lunchtime and find my favourites: a turkey sandwich and a pear! I would go to my friend's house after school to do homework and play.

That would be my perfect day.

ISBN: 978-1-897164-29-7

A. Unscramble the letters and write the writer's favourite things.

1.

cyulk rchma

_____

2.

uktyre nwsdcahi

_____

3.

insngig disrb

_____

4.

pgrdroie

_____

5.

apre

_____

6.

lube sedrs

_____

B. Draw your favourite thing. Write a sentence to go with it.

_____

ISBN: 978-1-897164-29-7

Connecting Words – And / Or

"**And**" and "**or**" are **connecting words**. They can be used to join words.

"And" is used to join items in a list to show addition.
"Or" is used to join options to show choices.

Examples: Shirley has three toonies <u>and</u> two dimes.

I think either Jen <u>or</u> Dennis will win.

C.   Circle ◯ the correct words to complete the sentences.

1. Fries   and / or   pizza are my favourites.

2. Shall we watch a cartoon   and / or   a movie at five?

3. Is this a robin   and / or   a sparrow?

4. I made two new friends today. They are Jessica   and / or   Miranda.

5. I can see some birds   and / or   squirrels outside the window.

6. Which dress do you like, the pink one   and / or   the blue one?

ISBN: 978-1-897164-29-7

D. Look at the pictures. Complete the sentences with "and" or "or".

1.

On which day are we setting out, _____ ?

2.

Who is taller, _____

_____ ?

3.

We will need to get these from the grocery store: _____

_____ .

4.

Which present do you like better,

_____

_____ ?

5.

Don't forget to take _____

_____

_____ with you.

ISBN: 978-1-897164-29-7

Riddles

Riddles are questions that have funny answers. They are like guessing games. Can you answer these questions?

I have a face, but I don't have eyes, or a nose, or a mouth.

I have two hands, but they don't have fingers.

What am I?

Answer: a clock

I have four legs, and you can sit on me.

But...I also have two arms!

What am I?

Answer: an armchair

What starts with "p", ends with "e", and has lots of letters?

Answer: a post office

Letters make up words. Letters are also found at a post office.

ISBN: 978-1-897164-29-7

A. Solve these riddles.

1.

I have teeth but I won't bite.
I'm a good friend of your hair.
What am I?

_____

2.

I have no legs but I can run.
You can see me but you can't hold me with your hands.
What am I?

_____

B. Think of your own riddle. Write it on the lines. Draw a funny picture to go with it.

_____

_____

_____

_____

ISBN: 978-1-897164-29-7

Connecting Word – But

"**But**" is used to join two contrasting ideas in a sentence.

Example: Chickens have wings <u>but</u> they cannot fly.

C. **Check ✔ the correct sentences.**

1. Jerry likes chocolate but he likes toffee. ☐

2. The road was slippery but he fell. ☐

3. The weather is nice today but we have to stay at home. ☐

4. The words are small but we can still read them. ☐

5. The song is good but he sings it badly. ☐

6. Nicole wants to join the camp but she is too young. ☐

7. Let's buy an ice cream but share it together. ☐

ISBN: 978-1-897164-29-7

D. Add "but" with a ∧ at the correct places in the sentences.

1. The movie was long we did not find it boring.

2. This dish doesn't look nice it tastes good.

3. The girls play volleyball the boys play soccer.

4. The sun is shining it is also raining.

5. I want to eat a popsicle there are not any left.

E. Join the two parts with "but" to complete the sentences.

- it is friendly
- the sea water is cool
- this one is too sour
- I can reach it

1. Ivan likes juice _____ .

2. The shelf is tall _____ .

3. The dog looks fierce _____ .

4. The sand is hot _____ .

ISBN: 978-1-897164-29-7

One day, a fox was walking in the jungle. Suddenly, a tiger jumped on the fox. The fox cried out, "I am the King of the Jungle. How dare you try to hurt me!"

The tiger looked at him. He was very surprised. "You are not the King of the Jungle. You are just a fox."

"I am the King," said the fox. "All the animals are afraid of me! Come with me and I'll show you."

The tiger followed the fox. They came upon a herd of deer. When the deer saw the tiger behind the fox, they ran away in fright! Then the fox and the tiger came to some monkeys.

The King of the Jungle

The monkeys saw the tiger behind the fox, and they also ran away.

The fox turned to the tiger. "You see how the animals run away when they see me?"

"You are truly the King of the Jungle," said the tiger. He bowed low and let the fox run proudly away.

ISBN: 978-1-897164-29-7

A. Write the names of the animals.

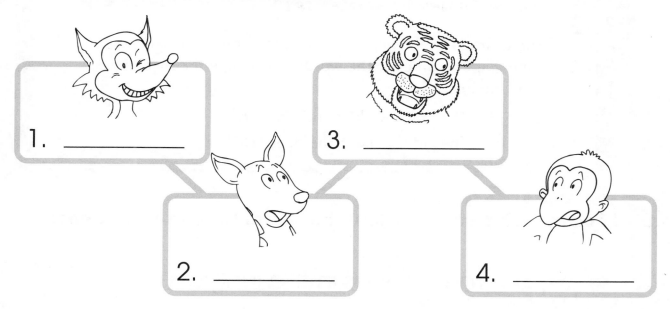

1. _____

2. _____

3. _____

4. _____

B. Put the sentences in order. Write them on the lines.

- The monkeys also ran away.
- The deer were frightened and ran away.
- The fox said that he was the King of the Jungle.
- The tiger tried to catch the fox.
- The fox ran proudly away.
- The tiger bowed to the fox.

1. _____

2. _____

3. _____

4. _____

5. _____

6. _____

ISBN: 978-1-897164-29-7

Word Order in Sentences

The words in a sentence should be put in order to make sense. Changing the order of the words can change the meaning of the sentence.

Example: The dog is walking the girl. (✘)

The girl is walking the dog. (✔)

C. Look at each picture. Colour the of the correct sentence.

1.  The fox was in the jungle.

   The jungle was in the fox.

2.  The rabbit chases the fox.

   The fox chases the rabbit.

3. The sun is behind the clouds.

   The clouds are behind the sun.

4.  The cat is eating the fish.

   The fish is eating the cat.

ISBN: 978-1-897164-29-7

D. Put the words in order to write the sentences.

Remember to begin each sentence with a capital letter and end it with the correct punctuation mark.

1. like   cheese   mice   eating

_____

2. colourful   flowers   the   are

_____

3. puts   the   she   box   toys   in   the

_____

4. is   a   writing   Benny   letter

_____

5. ice cream   who   strawberry   wants

_____

6. the   hiding   dog   candy   is   the

_____

7. you   are   where   going

_____

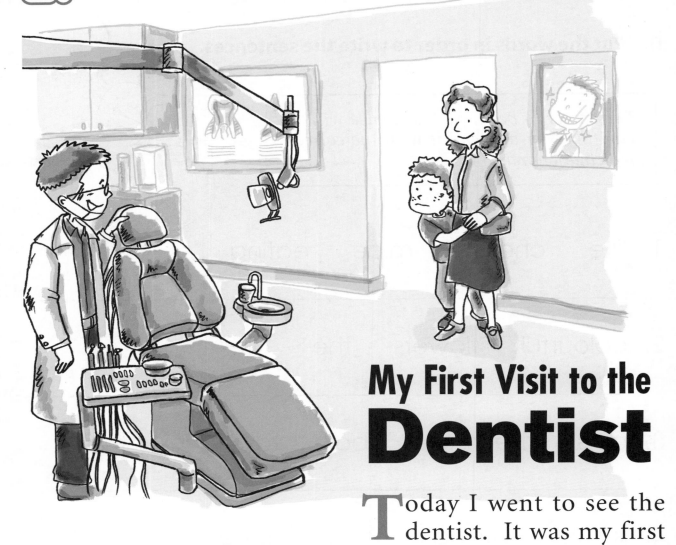

My First Visit to the
Dentist

Today I went to see the dentist. It was my first time. I was a little scared, but the dentist was very kind. He told me to sit down on the big chair. We watched a cartoon about a mouse having his teeth checked. It was funny.

Then the dentist showed me some of his tools. Later, I pressed a button, and some water went into the drinking cup.

After that, the dentist told me to lie back and open my mouth. He counted my teeth. Then he checked them carefully. He said my teeth looked nice. He showed me how to brush them correctly. When I was leaving, he gave me a new toothbrush!

I like my dentist. I will go back to see him again in six months.

ISBN: 978-1-897164-29-7

A. **Find words from the story that match the meanings below. Circle ◯ them in the word search.**

- good
- large
- the opposite of "front"
- You use it to brush your teeth.

- pushed
- frightened
- the opposite of "close"
- You use it to drink water.

k	k	a	q	t	f	d	n	r	e	r	b	l	i
b	a	y	b	p	r	e	s	s	e	d	p	a	x
c	n	e	i	z	h	x	c	o	l	j	s	w	c
u	i	c	g	b	r	j	a	z	b	a	c	k	m
s	c	a	r	e	d	y	b	c	v	m	u	t	s
n	e	u	l	r	d	n	e	h	w	o	p	e	n
t	o	o	t	h	b	r	u	s	h	p	h	o	k
t	e	v	b	u	m	s	g	a	c	z	e	w	b

B. **Give short answers to the questions.**

1. How did the writer feel when he went to see the dentist?

_____

2. What was the cartoon about?

_____

3. When will the writer see the dentist again?

_____

ISBN: 978-1-897164-29-7

Related Sentences

We put sentences that are related together. They should be about the same topic.

Example: The dentist checked my teeth. ~~I want to be a dentist too.~~ Then he showed me how to brush them.

C. Read each group of sentences. Put a line through the one that is not related to the others.

1. We are dining out this evening. We will try the new Italian restaurant nearby. The food there is nice. John is hungry.

2. There are many people at the beach. Some of them are swimming and some are sunbathing. It is too cold to go to the beach in winter.

3. Those puppies are cute. We have a new dog. He has a long, brown body. We call him Sausage.

ISBN: 978-1-897164-29-7

D. Write the sentences below in the correct places.

- She will get her eighth teddy bear this summer.
- My aunt has a candy shop.
- He goes fishing every weekend in summer.

1.

_____

_____

It sells candies of different shapes and flavours.

I like the lollipops best.

2.

My dad loves fishing.

_____

_____

I sometimes go with him.

3.

Carrie collects teddy bears.

Her uncle sends her a teddy bear for her birthday every year.

_____

_____

ISBN: 978-1-897164-29-7

A Day with Grandpa

I like it when Grandpa comes to visit. He always does amazing things with us. Today he said we were going to make a bird feeder!

First, Grandpa took out a pine cone and a bag of birdseed. He told me to get the peanut butter and put some all over the pine cone. Then he told my sister to roll the pine cone in the birdseed.

Next, Grandpa tied a strong string around the pine cone. We went outside and walked to a tree in the backyard. Grandpa tied the pine cone to a branch.

We waited. Soon a bird came and pecked at the pine cone! Grandpa said it was a sparrow. Later, a beautiful blue bird came to get some seeds. Grandpa said it was a blue jay. It was exciting! We like watching birds with Grandpa.

ISBN: 978-1-897164-29-7

A. Look at the picture clues. Complete the crossword puzzle.

Sequencing

Sentences should be put in a logical order so that people can follow the idea.

B. Match the sentences with the pictures. Write the letters.

A He then tied the pine cone to a branch.

B I put peanut butter over a pine cone.

C Grandpa tied a string around the pine cone.

D I got the peanut butter from the fridge.

E Soon a bird came and pecked at the pine cone.

F Then my sister rolled the pine cone in birdseed.

1.

2.

3.

4.

5.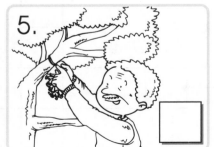

6.

ISBN: 978-1-897164-29-7

C. **Put the sentences in (B) in order. Write them on the lines below.**

1. _____

2. _____

3. _____

4. _____

5. _____

6. _____

D. **Put the pictures in order by writing the letters in the boxes. Write sentences about them.**

⬜ _____

⬜ _____

⬜ _____

ISBN: 978-1-897164-29-7

A. **Morris the Mouse and his family have moved into a new home. Rewrite what they say correctly.**

> *Use capital letters to begin sentences and proper nouns, and for "I", days of the week, months of the year, and festival names.*
>
> *End a telling sentence with a ".", an asking sentence with a "?", and a surprising sentence with an "!".*

1. what a big kitchen

   _____

2. we can have a big feast here at christmas

   _____

   _____

3. can i invite jim and ross to come this sunday

   _____

   _____

4. oh no this family has a cat

   _____

ISBN: 978-1-897164-29-7

B. Circle ⃝ the subject of each sentence. Write the pronoun that can replace it on the line.

The subject of a sentence tells whom or what the sentence is about. It is usually a noun and it can be replaced by a pronoun (he, she, it, they, I, you, we).

CHEESE

Fat-Free

24 slices

1. Morris finds a pack of cheese on the floor. _____

2. The cheese looks yummy. _____

3. Gigi and Didi are jumping for joy. _____

4. The noise attracts Kevin the Cat. _____

5. Gigi screams at the sight of Kevin. _____

6. You and I had better run. _____

7. The mice scurry back to the hole. _____

8. Molly is panting heavily. _____

C. Morris and his family are clever. Read the sentences and complete the crossword puzzle.

There is an **A** on the table.

The mice **2** to get it.

Morris **B** up a string to the table.

He **3** the apple with all his might.

The apple **C** to the floor.

They **1** the apple into their hole.

roll

climbs

apple

want

falls

pushes

ISBN: 978-1-897164-29-7

D. Circle ◯ the correct location word to complete each sentence.

A location word shows where someone or something is.

1.

Morris finds nothing in / over the box.

2.

Kevin the Cat is on / under the table.

3.

The toy cat is beside / behind the mice.

4.

Molly is looking at a fly on / over her head.

5.

Morris hides himself under / behind the door.

ISBN: 978-1-897164-29-7

E. **The mice are having a family meeting. Fill in each blank with "and", "or", or "but".**

Use "and" to join items in a list to show addition.
Use "or" to join options to show choices.
Use "but" to join two contrasting ideas in a sentence.

 Should we move to a new home 1._____ stay?

 Kevin is big 2._____ fat 3._____ he's not fierce at all.

 Yes. He's good to his toy mouse 4._____ he never does us any harm.

 Sometimes he sees us getting food from the kitchen 5._____ he just lets us go.

 Actually, I think he's nice 6._____ I want to make friends with him.

 We can give him a present, maybe a fish 7._____ some cat food. I'm sure he wants to be our friend too.

ISBN: 978-1-897164-29-7

F. **Put the words in order to form sentences. Then write the letters to complete what the mice say.**

The words in a sentence should be put in order to make sense.

Sentences that are put together should be related.

1. **A** toy   Kevin   a   mouse   has

_____

B Kevin   every   milk   drinks   day

_____

C likes   it   he   with   playing

_____

◯ *does not belong to this group.*

2. **D** mouse   the   cute   toy   is

_____

E is   back   there   on   key   a   its

_____

F the   is   where   key

_____

◯ *does not belong to this group.*

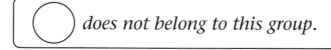

ISBN: 978-1-897164-29-7

ISBN: 978-1-897164-29-7

ISBN: 978-1-897164-29-7

This Is Me

We each have different things to tell about ourselves, like who we are, where we live, and what we look like.

A. Write about you. Then put in your photo.

Name:

_____ _____ _____
First   Middle   Last

Names of **Buddies** :

_____

_____

Favourite Things:

Game : _____

Sport : _____

Food : _____

Colour : _____

ISBN: 978-1-897164-29-7

B. **Draw a picture of you. Then fill in the blanks.**

My eyes are the colour _____ .

My hair is the colour _____ .

I am _____ centimetres tall.

I am _____ years old.

My Life in a Timeline

A timeline shows where things happen in time.

This timeline starts on the day you were born. Write down your birthday. Then draw a picture for each year to show what you did at that age.

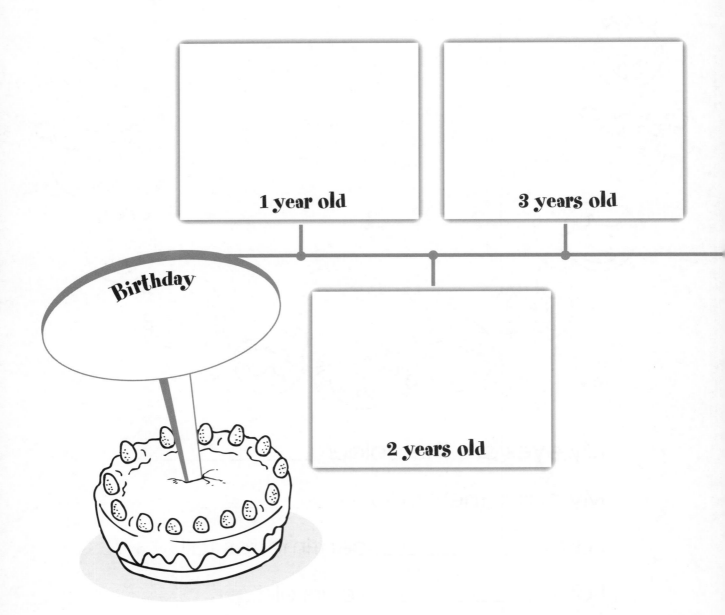

Birthday

1 year old

2 years old

3 years old

ISBN: 978-1-897164-29-7

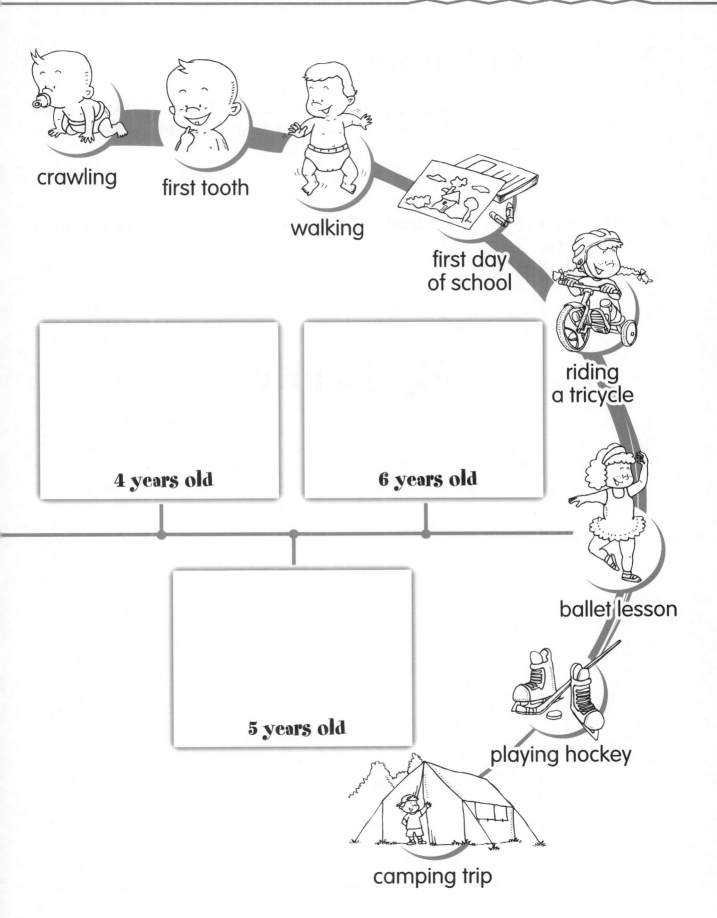

crawling

first tooth

walking

first day
of school

riding
a tricycle

4 years old

6 years old

5 years old

ballet lesson

playing hockey

camping trip

ISBN: 978-1-897164-29-7

My Family

Some families are big, and some families are small. Whatever the size, people in a family take care of one another. Doing different jobs is one way of doing that.

A. **Put in a photo of your family. Then write the names of your family members.**

My Family

photo

In my family, there are _____

_____

_____

ISBN: 978-1-897164-29-7

B. Check ✔ the home that looks like yours.

C. Write the names of your family members in the chart. Check ✔ the jobs each person does.

Person \ Job	Make breakfast	Feed pet	Make bed	Wash dishes	Tidy up toys
Me					

ISBN: 978-1-897164-29-7

Responsibilities and Rules (1)

We have responsibilities and rules at home, at school, and in our community. Some rules keep us safe. Others help us work and play together.

A. Match each child's responsibility with the picture.

1. I feed my cat every day.

2. I help my sister reach for a cup.

3. I water my plants when they are dry.

4. I return my books to the library.

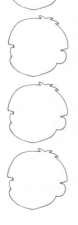

ISBN: 978-1-897164-29-7

B. Circle ◯ the rule that goes with each picture. The first one is done for you.

1.
Wait in Line
(Wear Helmet)

2.
No Littering
No Running

3.
Wash Hands
Wait in Line

4.
Do Not Walk on Grass
Keep Dogs on Leash

C. Look at this picture. Write a rule that your family might have.

_____

_____

ISBN: 978-1-897164-29-7

5

Responsibilities and Rules (2)

Rules in the community help us get along with one another. When we follow these rules, we are being **courteous**. But sometimes rules need to **change** and we make new ones.

A. **How can we be courteous? Write the letters of the rules.**

A. Say "please" and "thank you".

B. Use indoor voice.

C. Say "I'm sorry".

D. Put toys away.

E. Wait in line.

F. Share.

ISBN: 978-1-897164-29-7

B. **Read what the children say in the pictures. Then check ✔ the correct rules for the new situations.**

1.

We always let the youngest go first.

What if a guest comes to play?

(A) The guest goes last.

(B) The guest goes first.

2.

I need a coat to go outside.

What if it is summer?

(A) Wear sunscreen.

(B) Wear mittens.

3.

I go to bed at 9 o'clock.

What if you are older?

(A) Bedtime is earlier.

(B) Bedtime is later.

ISBN: 978-1-897164-29-7

6

Responsibilities, Rules, and Relationships

Responsibilities and rules help us build relationships. For example, if we have a pet, we need to take care of it and follow rules in public. That is how we build relationships with our pet and with our community.

Sam's dog is lost in the park. Help Sam answer the questions to find it.

1. Which sign tells dog owners to keep their dogs close to them? Colour it.

p Do not litter

r No feeding

l Keep dogs on leash

m Wet Paint Keep off

ISBN: 978-1-897164-29-7

2. Which question shows courtesy? Colour it.

o *Excuse me. Did you see my dog?*

a *Hey! Did you see my dog?*

3. Who showed responsibility for the lost dog? Colour the picture.

t   s   g   b

4. Look at what you have coloured. What are the letters? Write them in the spaces below.

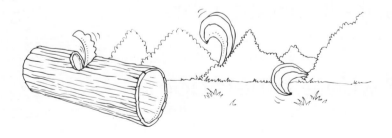

Sam's dog is in the ___ ___ ___ .

7

The Community

Our community is the space we and our **neighbours** share. We may work, play, and learn in our community too.

A. Match the riddles with the pictures. Write the correct letters.

A Our neighbours are too far away to be seen

We grow food on the land that is in between

B Our roads are many

Our buildings are tall

Museums and shops

There is something for all

C Fish to eat – it was caught today

We live where others come to play

ISBN: 978-1-897164-29-7

B. Choose the correct word for each picture. Then cross out ✗ what does not belong.

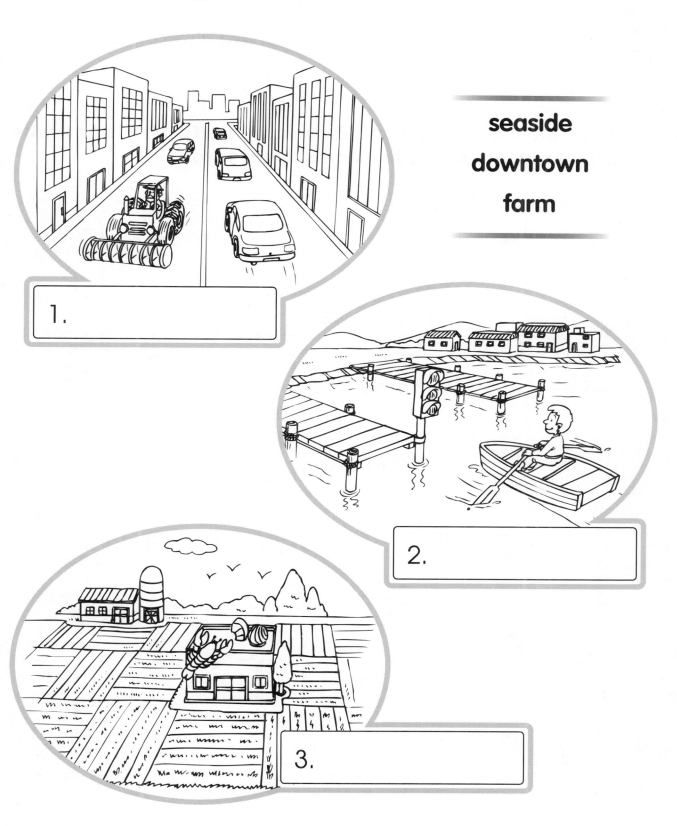

seaside

downtown

farm

1.

2.

3.

ISBN: 978-1-897164-29-7

The Community Up Close

People in a community need clean water, food, shelter, and services that help them live better. They also need places for fun and places for exercise.

A. Below are some things that a community needs. Match the words with the pictures. The first one is done for you.

| | A |
| ABC | |

postal service | F | T |

homes

food

health care

school

police

ISBN: 978-1-897164-29-7

B. **Find and colour the places for fun or exercise. Then answer the questions.**

1.

2. Where do you go to see movies? _____

3. Where do you go swimming? _____

4. Where do you go to play on the swings? _____

5. Name some fun places in your community.

_____

ISBN: 978-1-897164-29-7

Out and About (1)

There are many different ways to **travel** around a community. For example, children may travel to school in different ways.

A. How do these people travel? Choose the correct words.

bus
walk
horse
bicycle
taxi
car

274

ISBNISBN: 978-1-897164-29-7

B. Make a graph to show how these children travel to school. Then answer the questions.

A graph lets us compare the different ways people travel.

Jackson Public School

First, count how many children walk. For each child that walks, colour one ☺ . Then do the same for the others.

1. Walk ☺ ☺ ☺ ☺ ☺ ☺ ☺

   Bike ☺ ☺ ☺ ☺ ☺ ☺ ☺

   Bus   ☺ ☺ ☺ ☺ ☺ ☺ ☺

   Car   ☺ ☺ ☺ ☺ ☺ ☺ ☺

2. How do most of the children travel to school? _____

3. How do you travel to school? _____

ISBN: 978-1-897164-29-7

10

Out and About (2)

We need to follow signs when we travel around our community. They are there to keep us safe.

A. **Match the signs with what these people say. Write the correct letters.**

A — PEDESTRIAN

B — STOP

C

D

1.

I cross the road only when this is on.

_____

2.

I don't ride my bike here.

_____

3.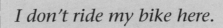

I look carefully and cross the road here.

_____

4.

I stop my car when I see this sign.

_____

ISBN: 978-1-897164-29-7

B. **Read these rules. Then match them with the signs. Write the correct letters.**

1. No running in the school hallways. ☐

2. Keep out of the school parking lot. ☐

3. School area: drive slowly. ☐

4. Slippery floor: walk carefully. ☐

A

B

C

D

WET
FLOOR

C. **Think of a new rule for your school. Draw a sign and write about it.**

_____

_____

_____

_____

_____

ISBN: 978-1-897164-29-7

11

Working in the Community

There are many different **jobs** in a community.

A. Find the worker doing each job. Write the correct letter on the line.

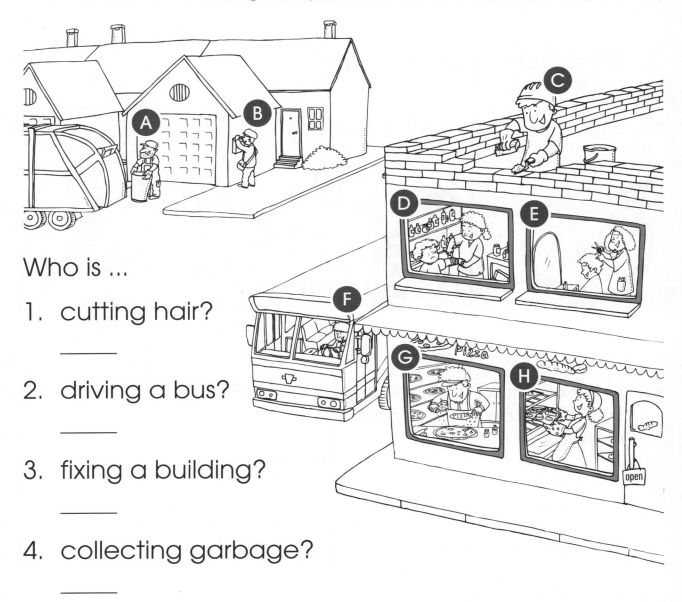

Who is ...

1. cutting hair?

    ____

2. driving a bus?

    ____

3. fixing a building?

    ____

4. collecting garbage?

    ____

5. helping a boy? ____   6. baking bread? ____

7. making pizza? ____   8. carrying mail? ____

ISBN: 978-1-897164-29-7

B. **Read about each job. Check ✔ the worker that fits.**

1. I work outdoors.

2. I help people who are hurt.

3. I use a comb and scissors to do my job.

4. I take people where they need to go.

12

Service Workers

Workers in a community produce many different things.

A. Match the workers with their work and products. Write the correct letters.

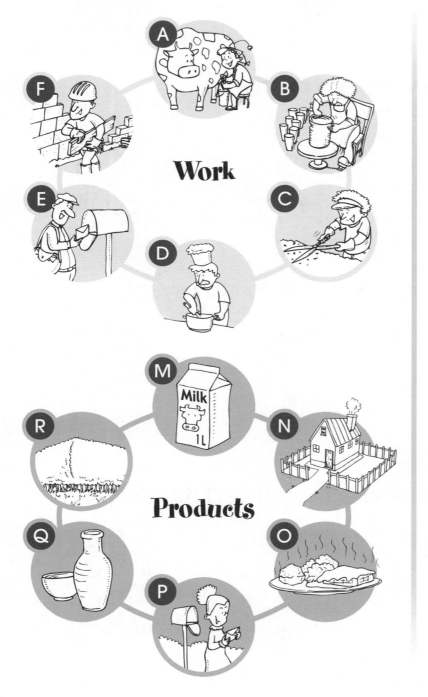

Work

Products

1. chef

   ____ ____

2. farmer

   ____ ____

3. mailman

   ____ ____

4. construction worker

   ____ ____

5. landscaper

   ____ ____

6. potter

   ____ ____

ISBN: 978-1-897164-29-7

B. The worker is missing in each picture. Choose the correct word to complete the crossword puzzle.

truck driver
caretaker
teacher
cashier
artist

Safety Workers

Police officers and **firefighters** are some of the people who help keep us safe. They use special **tools** to do their jobs.

A. Put the pictures in order. Write 1 to 3.

1.

2.

ISBN: 978-1-897164-29-7

B. Match the tools with the workers. Write the correct letters.

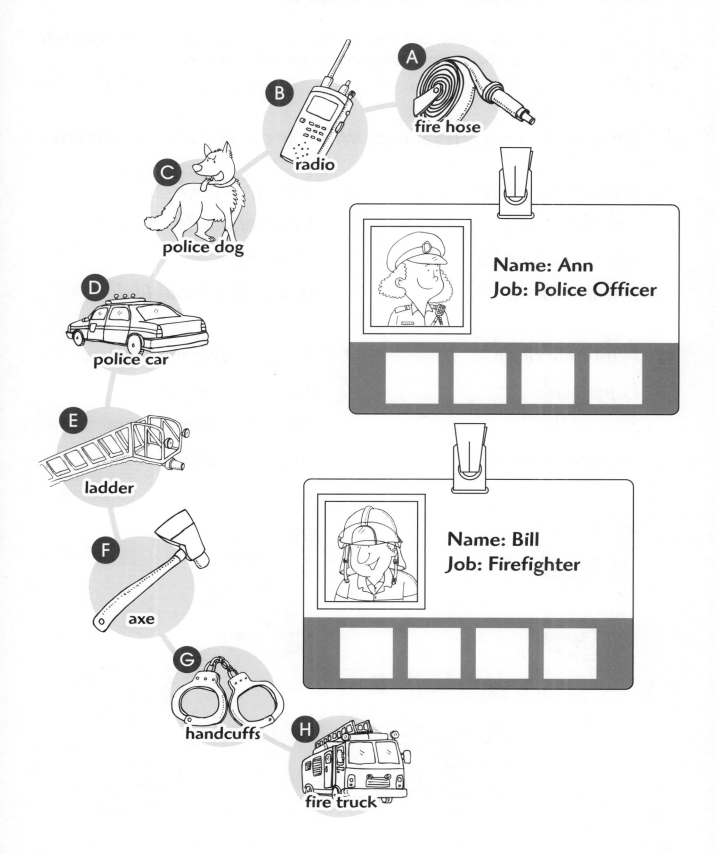

A fire hose

B radio

C police dog

D police car

E ladder

F axe

G handcuffs

H fire truck

Name: Ann
Job: Police Officer

Name: Bill
Job: Firefighter

ISBN: 978-1-897164-29-7

14

Health Workers

There are many different health workers in the community. They help us stay healthy and they help us get well when we are sick.

A. What are these rhymes about? Write the correct letters on the lines.

1. If books and things
   Are hard to see
   The _____'s office
   Is where I'll be

2. A fever, a cough
   A case of the flu
   I'll visit the _____
   That's what I should do

3. I sit in the chair
   I open wide
   So now the _____
   May look inside

4. A _____ gives me care
   Whenever I'm sick
   And helps to make sure
   That the healing is quick

doctor

dentist

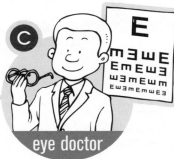

eye doctor

nurse

ISBN: 978-1-897164-29-7

B.   Match the workers with their names.   Write the correct letters.

A veterinarian

B nurse

C pharmacist

D dentist

E doctor

F ambulance driver

1. Ann works in a pharmacy and gives people their medicine.

2. Bill helps animals get well when they are sick.

3. Sue talks to children at school about health.

4. Tom gets people to the hospital quickly.

5. Jan helps people take care of their teeth.

6. Rob helps people get well when they are sick.

ISBN: 978-1-897164-29-7

15

Looking at Community Workers

Many of our community workers wear **uniforms**. Some of them also need special **vehicles** to do their work.

Match the workers with their uniforms. Then match the vehicles with the workers. Write the correct letters.

Uniform

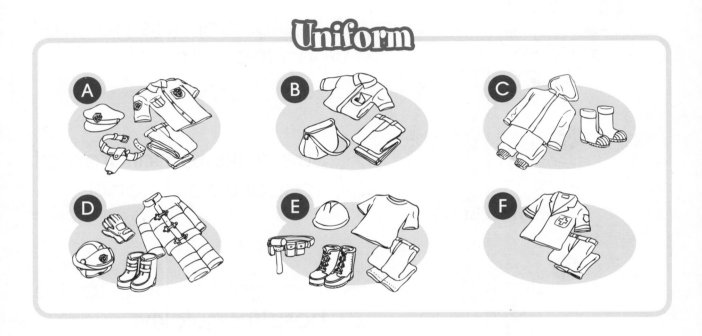

1. _____ _____

2. _____ _____

3. _____ _____

ISBN: 978-1-897164-29-7

Vehicle

M

N

O

P

Q

R

4. _____ _____

5. _____ _____

6. _____ _____

ISBN: 978-1-897164-29-7

16

Simple Maps and Directions

Maps have **symbols** that show where things are. When there is no map, we can use words like "**left**", "**right**", "**above**", and "**below**" to tell where something is.

A. Use the symbols to understand this map. Then answer the questions.

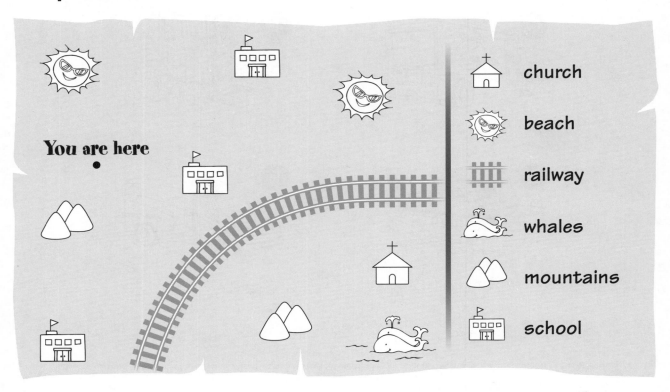

church
beach
railway
whales
mountains
school

1. Which is closer to you, a school or the church? _____

2. What is farthest away from you? _____

3. How many beaches are there? _____

4. How many schools are there? _____

ISBN: 978-1-897164-29-7

B. **Where did Sue and Tom put their toys on the shelf? Write the correct words.**

1. **left**
   right

   The toy car is to the _____ of the toy train.

2. **left**
   right

   The football is to the _____ of the skateboard.

3. **above**
   below

   The teddy bear is Sue's favourite. It is _____ the letter blocks.

4. **above**
   below

   The toy train is _____ the puppet and _____ the skateboard.

17

Looking at a Grid

Besides maps, we can also use grids to show where things are. To show what is on a grid, we can use **symbols** and **colour**.

A. **Look at the grid. Name the grid squares where things appear. Then draw two more things on the grid.**

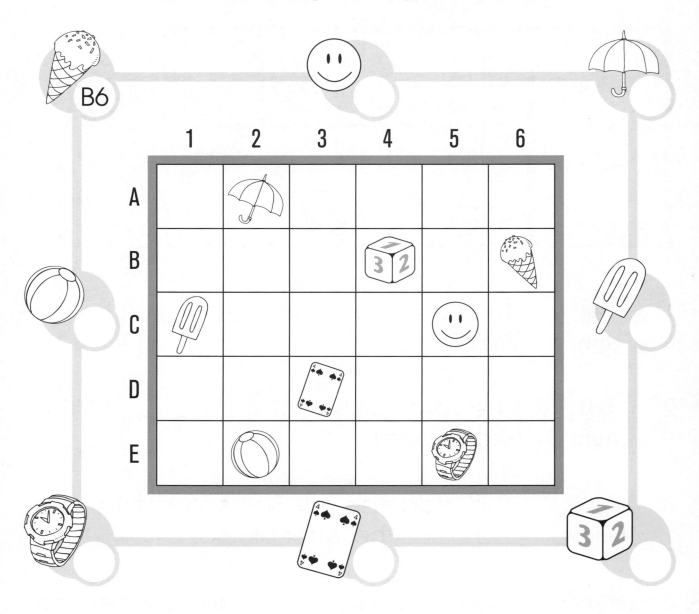

- Draw a 🍃 in A1 and a 🏠 in C3.

ISBN: 978-1-897164-29-7

B. **Tom and Sue are looking at a map. Colour to show what is there. Then add a few more things on it.**

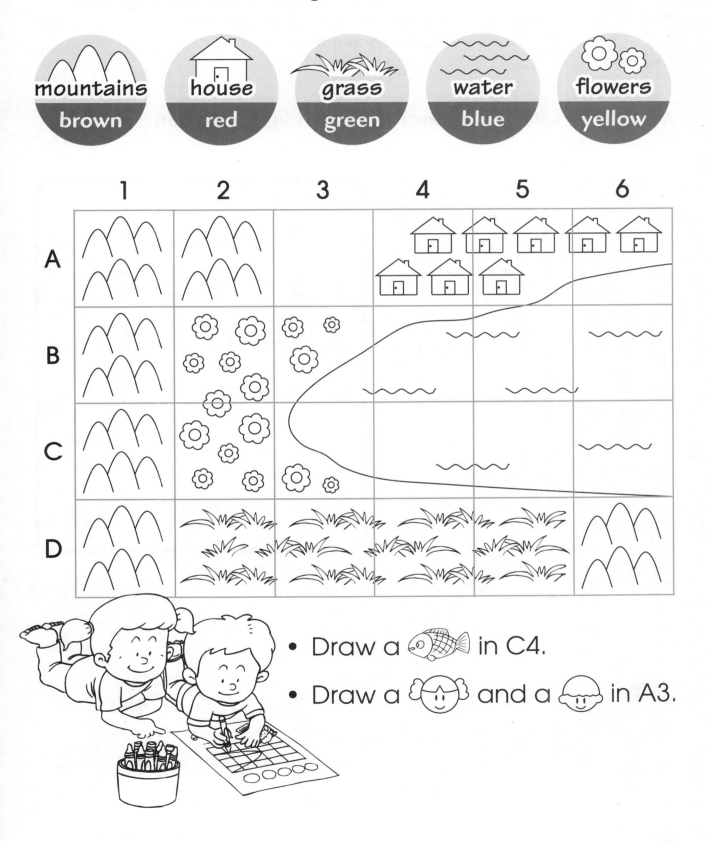

- Draw a 🐟 in C4.
- Draw a 👧 and a 👦 in A3.

ISBN: 978-1-897164-29-7

18

Streets and Distances

Maps can tell us **how far** it is from one place to another. They also show the streets of a **community**.

A. How far is it? Count the number of logs to find out.

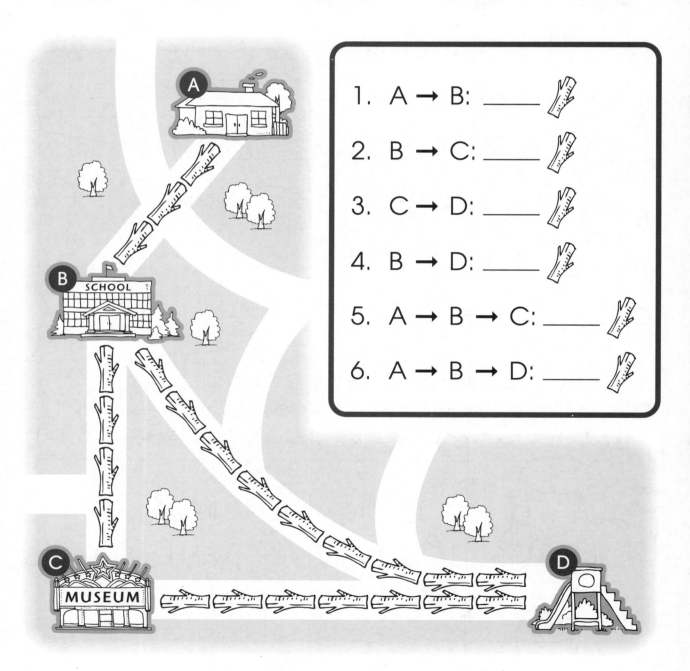

1. A ➔ B: _____
2. B ➔ C: _____
3. C ➔ D: _____
4. B ➔ D: _____
5. A ➔ B ➔ C: _____
6. A ➔ B ➔ D: _____

ISBN: 978-1-897164-29-7

B. **Look at the map of Ben's community. Circle ◯ the correct answers or fill in the blanks.**

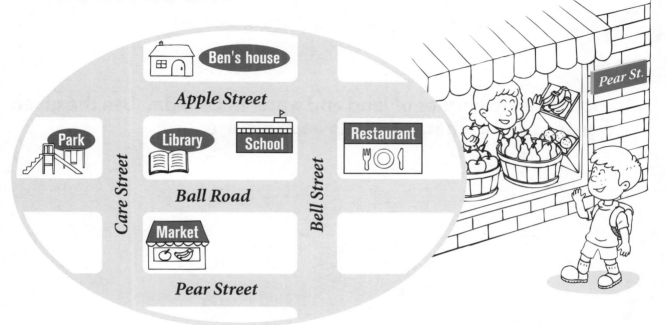

1. The school is at the corner of Apple Street / Pear Street and Bell Street.

2. At the corner of Care Street and Pear Street, there is a library / market .

3.
My house is at the _____ of _____ and _____ .

Ben

4. The restaurant is where Bell Street crosses _____ .

19

Land and Water in Canada

Canada is a huge country, with lots of land and water.

A. **Look at the examples of land and water in Canada. Use the given words to write what you see in each picture.**

1 _____

2 _____

mountains
waterfall
plains
ocean
river
lake

3 _____

4 _____

5 _____

6 _____

ISBN: 978-1-897164-29-7

B. Find and circle ◯ the words from (A).

a	e	s	t	r	w	b	a		w
w	a	t	e	r	f	a	l	l	a
a	p	b	u			o	k	t
a	l	l	e			c	a	e
o	u	l	a	k	e		e	a	r
u	t	e	i		u	r	a	n	a
n	g	s	n		a	o	n
t	h	y	s		d	e	u
m	o	u	n	t	a	i	n	s	t
r			r	i	v	e	r	t	s	u
j			z	w	b	c	x	a	v	c

C. Circle ◯ the correct word for each group.

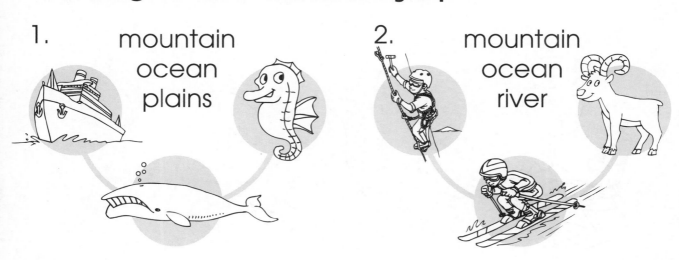

1. mountain
   ocean
   plains

2. mountain
   ocean
   river

20

Animals in Canada

Canada is home to many animals.

A. Paul cut out the shapes of some Canadian animals. Match each one with its name. Write the correct letter.

A. polar bear

B. squirrel

C. moose

D. snowy owl

E. whale

F. blue jay

G. seal

H. bat

ISBN: 978-1-897164-29-7

B. What are these animals? Complete the crossword puzzle with the given words.

porcupine   buffalo   sea lion

fox   loon   lynx

ISBN: 978-1-897164-29-7

21

Knowing Our Environment

Our environment is the place where we live, work, and play. Some places are **natural**, and some are **human-built**. Sometimes, they even look like one another.

A. Look at these places. Write the correct letters.

A

B

C

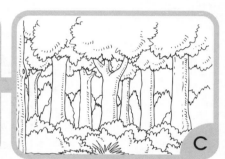

D

Natural: _____

Human-built: _____

E

H

G

F

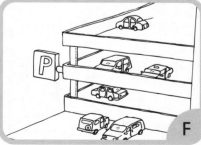

ISBN: 978-1-897164-29-7

B. Match each natural environment with the human-built environment that looks like it. Write the correct letter.

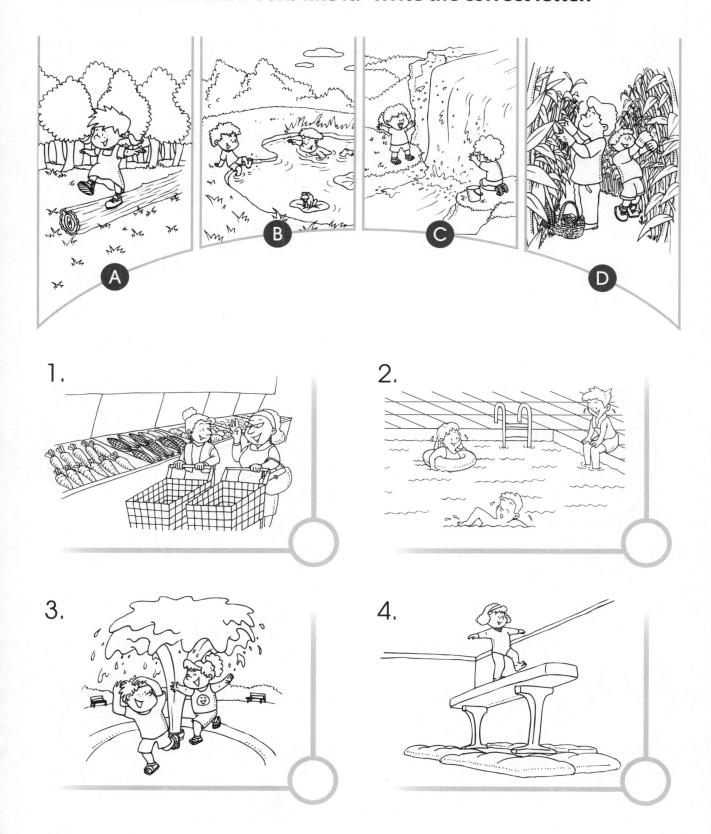

22

Caring for Our Environment

We must take care of our environment to have clean air and water. Planting trees, **recycling**, and making less garbage are some of the things we can do.

A. What is the path that takes care of our environment? Colour the correct pictures to find out. Then draw a line on the path.

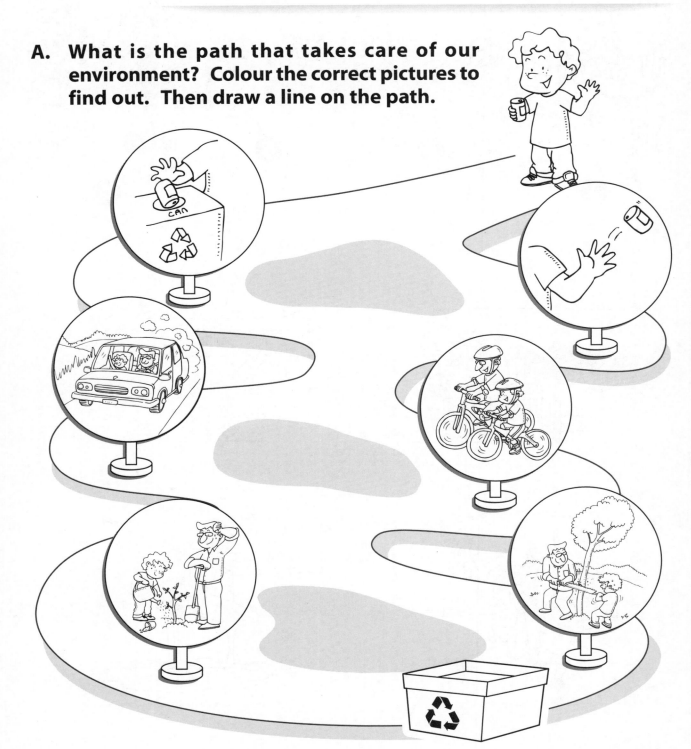

ISBN: 978-1-897164-29-7

B. For each pair of things, cross out **X** the one that will make more garbage.

1.

2.

3.

C. Circle ◯ the thing that does not belong in each group.

1.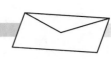

2.

3.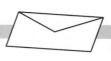

4.

ISBN: 978-1-897164-29-7

23

Smart Tools (1)

We have smart tools in our homes that make our lives easier.

A. Circle ◯ the correct tool for each picture.

1.

Ⓐ snowblower

Ⓑ television

Ⓒ lawn mower

2.

Ⓐ snowblower

Ⓑ television

Ⓒ lawn mower

3.

Ⓐ telephone

Ⓑ microwave

Ⓒ vacuum cleaner

ISBN: 978-1-897164-29-7

B. Which tool is needed for each activity? Write the correct letter.

1. writing an e-mail   _____

2. watching the news   _____

3. listening to music   _____

4. heating up food quickly   _____

5. getting light when it is night   _____

6. talking to a friend far away   _____

Smart Tools (2)

Tools look different in different places. They are smaller at home, but bigger in the world outside. Tools also look different through time. Many things from before look different today.

A. Match the small tools with the big tools. Write the correct letters.

1.

2.

3.

4.

ISBN: 978-1-897164-29-7

B.   Put the pictures in order from "before" to "today".   Write 1 to 3.

1.

2.

3.

ISBN: 978-1-897164-29-7

A. Put in a photo of you on the piece of paper. Write about you. Draw lines to tell who does each job at home. Then write your family members' names.

Name: _____ _____ (☺ / ☺)
First   Last

Birthday: ____ ____ ____
Day   Month   Year

🩶 My Favourite Things

- Toy: _____
- Food: _____
- Colour: _____

make breakfast •

tidy up toys •

cut grass •

bake cookies •

- Grandma _____
- Grandpa _____
- Mother _____
- Father _____
- Brother _____
- Sister _____

ISBN: 978-1-897164-29-7

B. **Your friends in class tell you how they travel to school and what community workers they want to be. Look at the pictures and read what they say. Then fill in the blanks.**

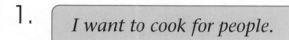

Way of Travel	Community Worker
bus car	dentist nurse
walk horse	farmer chef
bicycle	teacher

1.

I want to cook for people.

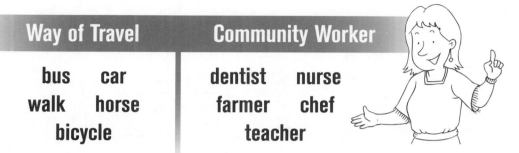

Way of Travel: _____

Job: _____

2.

I want to milk cows on a farm.

Way of Travel: _____

Job: _____

3.

I want to help people take care of their teeth.

Way of Travel: _____

Job: _____

ISBN: 978-1-897164-29-7

C. **You made a grid with your friends. Write the correct answers and finish what Bill says.**

1. a. Who drives the vehicle in C4? _____

   b. Where is he on the grid? _____

2. a. Who uses the tool in D3? _____

   b. Where is she on the grid? _____

3.

When I'm older, I want to drive the vehicle in D2. I'll wear the uniform in _____ .

ISBN: 978-1-897164-29-7

D. You also made a simple map. Circle ◯ the correct answers.

1. [school] / [theatre] is closer to the railway.

2. There is only one [library] / [school] .

3.

You are at [park]. What should you do?

A. Keep dogs on leash.

B. Use indoor voice.

school
park
pool
library
theatre
railway

4. You are at [library]. What should you do?

A. Wear a thick jacket.

B. Use indoor voice.

ISBN: 978-1-897164-29-7

E.   Write or circle ◯ the correct answers.

1.   What do we use to do the following?

   a. check e-mail: _____

   b. listen to music: _____

   c. call a friend: _____

   d. clean the floor: _____

2.   **G** is   above / below   **B**.

3.   **C** is to the   right / left   of **D**.

ISBN: 978-1-897164-29-7

F. **You and your friends dressed up as animals in class. Label the animals and places with the correct letters and words. Colour the place where the animals find food. Then circle ◯ the correct answers.**

Animals

A. whale
B. lobster
C. seal
D. polar bear

2. **Places**

plains   lake   ocean   mountains

a.
b.
c.
d.

1.

3. We all find food in the **lake / ocean** , which is a **natural / human-built** environment.

ISBN: 978-1-897164-29-7

ISBN: 978-1-897164-29-7

ISBN: 978-1-897164-29-7

My Body

- Our bodies have many useful parts.
- We use different parts of our bodies to do different things.

A. Fill in the missing letter for each part of the body.

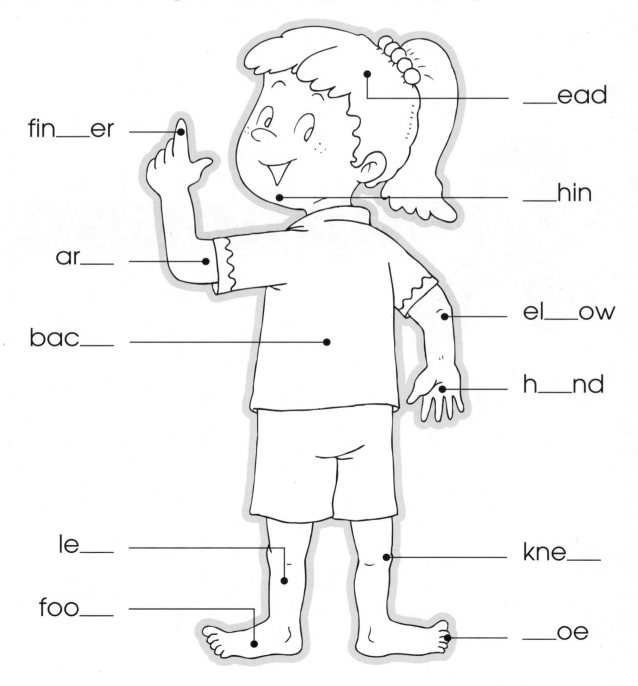

fin__er

ar__

bac__

le__

foo__

__ead

__hin

el__ow

h__nd

kne__

__oe

ISBN: 978-1-897164-29-7

B. Draw lines to match.

I jump with my ___ .

I drum with my ___ .

I play the guitar with my ___ .

I kick a ball with my ___ .

I bite with my ___ .

- fingers
- teeth
- legs
- foot
- hands

Five Senses

- *Our bodies have sense organs: our nose, tongue, eyes, ears, and skin.*
- *With our sense organs we can smell, taste, see, hear, and touch.*

A. Write the name of each sense organ. Then colour the correct picture to tell what each sense organ can do.

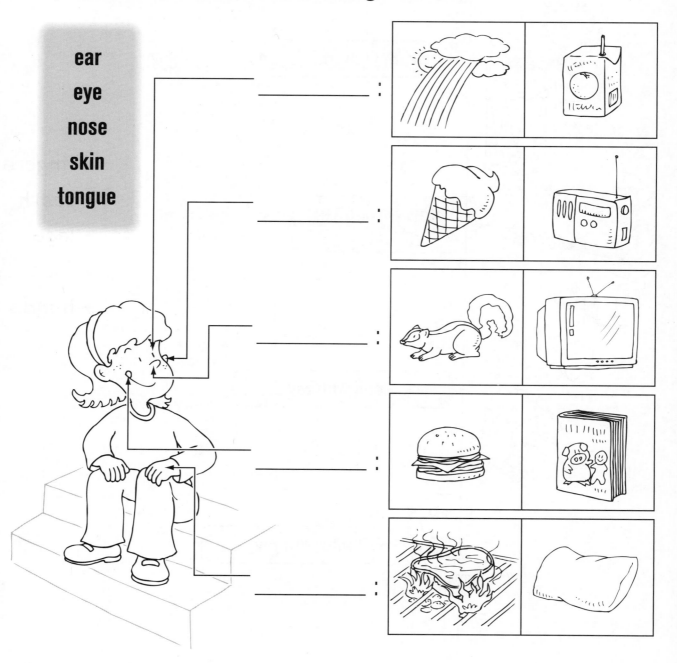

ear
eye
nose
skin
tongue

ISBN: 978-1-897164-29-7

B. Complete the following rhymes with the given words.

hearing, ears   touch, skin

taste, tongue   smell, nose

sight, eyes

Apple pie or

Red red rose

For my sense of 1._____

I use my 2._____

Warm, soft kittens

Make me grin

For my sense of 5._____

I use my 6._____

Ice cream here!

For old or young!

For my sense of 9._____

I use my 10._____

Watching the puck or

The early sunrise

For my sense of 3._____

I use my 4._____

The sound of a hit

The crowd cheers

For my sense of 7._____

I use my 8._____

ISBN: 978-1-897164-29-7

3

Our Senses at Work

- Our senses tell us all about the world.
- Our senses keep us safe.
- We also protect our sense organs.

A. Cross out ✗ the one that does not belong in each group.

1. **sense of hearing**

2. **sense of sight**

3. **sense of touch**

4. **sense of smell**

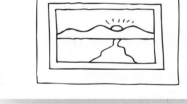

5. **sense of taste**

ISBN: 978-1-897164-29-7

B. Write the correct sense(s) to know the things below.

see   hear   touch   smell   taste

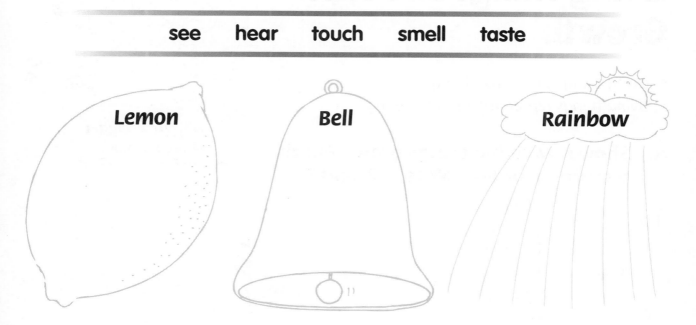

Lemon

Bell

Rainbow

C. Tell which group each item belongs to. Write the letters.

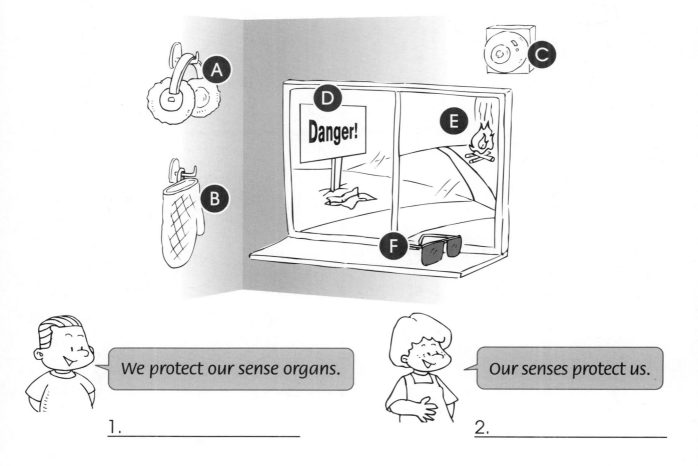

Danger!

We protect our sense organs.

Our senses protect us.

1._____

2._____

ISBN: 978-1-897164-29-7

4

Living Things and Their Growth

- Living things grow and change.
- Living things reproduce, or have young.

I will grow bigger just like my mom.

A. Show how living things grow. Put the pictures in order. Write 1, 2, and 3.

1.

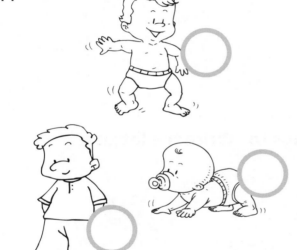

2.

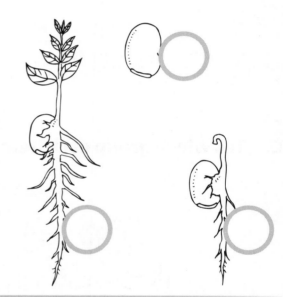

3.

4.

ISBN: 978-1-897164-29-7

B. Colour the living things in the picture.

ISBN: 978-1-897164-29-7

5

Needs of Living Things

- Living things need air, water, and food.
- Living things have different ways of getting what they need to live.

A. Match the pictures with what the boy says. Write the letters.

1. Living things need air. _____

2. Living things need water. _____

3. Living things need food. _____

ISBN: 978-1-897164-29-7

B. See what the living things get. Fill in the blanks with "air", "water", or "food".

Fish get _____ through their gills.

Plants get _____ through their roots.

Salamanders can get _____ through their skin.

Frogs catch _____ with their tongues.

Camels can store large amounts of _____ .

Plants make their own _____ with the help of the sun.

ISBN: 978-1-897164-29-7

Living Things and the Way They Move

- Our bodies let us move in many different ways.
- The way animals move depends on their bodies.

A. Describe how the animals move with the given words.

hop   swing   gallop   slither   climb   dive   fly

1. _____

2. _____

3.

4. _____

5. _____

6. _____

7. _____

  ISBN: 978-1-897164-29-7

B. Tell the movements in the picture.

| rolling | bouncing | throwing | diving | swinging |

1.

2.

3.

4.

5.

Patterns in Living Things

- Patterns are things that repeat.
- Some living things have patterns.

Honey, don't you think we have beautiful patterns?

A. Complete the patterns of the living things. Then name the living things.

tortoise   flower   bee   fish   pineapple   leaf

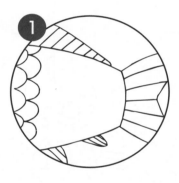

1. _____

2. _____

3. _____

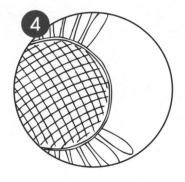

4. _____

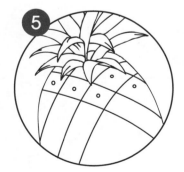

5. _____

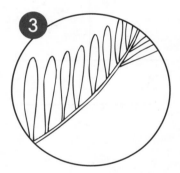

6. _____

ISBN: 978-1-897164-29-7

B. Sort the living things by their patterns. Write the letters.

spots: _____

rings: _____

spiral: _____

stripes: _____

8

Healthy Eating

- Canada's Food Guide helps us choose healthy food to eat.
- It is important to know where our food comes from.

> Mom, which one is the best?

A. **Look at the pictures. Sort them into the correct places. Write the letters.**

A   B   C  D

E  F 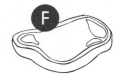 G  H

Food Guide

Grain Products	Vegetables and Fruits	Milk Products	Meat and Alternatives
◯	◯	◯	◯
◯	◯	◯	◯
◯	◯	◯	
◯	◯		
◯			
◯			

Enjoy a variety of foods from each group every day.

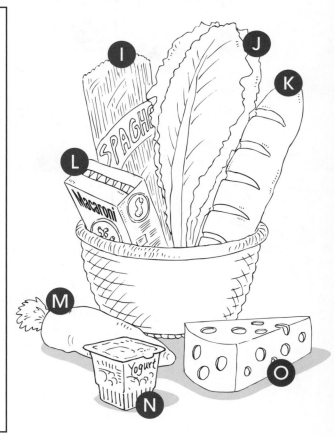

ISBN: 978-1-897164-29-7

B. Which food item is the healthiest choice in each group? Circle ⬭ it and fill in the missing letters to complete its name.

1. ___uic___

2. po___cor___

3. fr___sh ___rui___

C. The highlighted pictures show where our food comes from. Cross out ✗ the food that does not belong.

ISBN: 978-1-897164-29-7

9

Safe and Healthy Living

- There are things we can do to stay healthy: keep our bodies clean, exercise, and get plenty of sleep.
- Safety rules are important to know and follow.

A. Draw a line and colour the pictures to show David the path of healthy habits to reach the trophy.

David

Healthy Child

ISBN: 978-1-897164-29-7

B. **Look at the pictures. Give the people the things they need to be safe. Write the letters.**

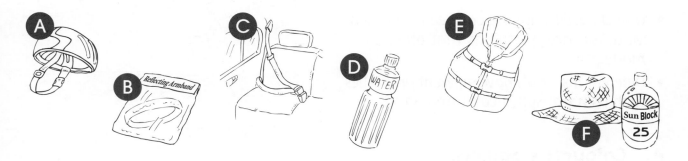

1.

2.

3.

4.

5.

6.

10

Objects and Materials

- Objects are things we can see and touch. Materials are the things that objects are made from.
- Different materials have different properties such as hard, soft, heavy, and light.

A. Colour the objects.

Objects made from
wood: brown
glass: blue
metal: yellow
cloth: green

ISBN: 978-1-897164-29-7

B. Describe the material of each object. Circle ⃝ the correct word.

1.

hard   soft

2.

light   heavy

3.

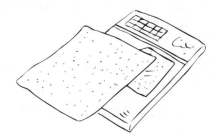

rough   smooth

4.

light
dark

5.

shiny   dull

C. Which material will make the object? Cross out ✗ the material that does not belong.

Shoe	Hard hat	Pillow
leather	glass	cloth
cement	metal	feathers
cloth	plastic	wood

ISBN: 978-1-897164-29-7

11

Materials that Join

- *Some materials can be used to join things together.*

A. Colour the sheets with the names of materials that join things to help the little spiral find the paper.

mortar · spoon · ice · bone

paper · thread · glue · stamp

rug · soap · nail · paint

picture · socks · snap · book

scissors · knife · zipper

ISBN: 978-1-897164-29-7

B. Match the materials that need to be joined with the materials that will join them. Write the letters.

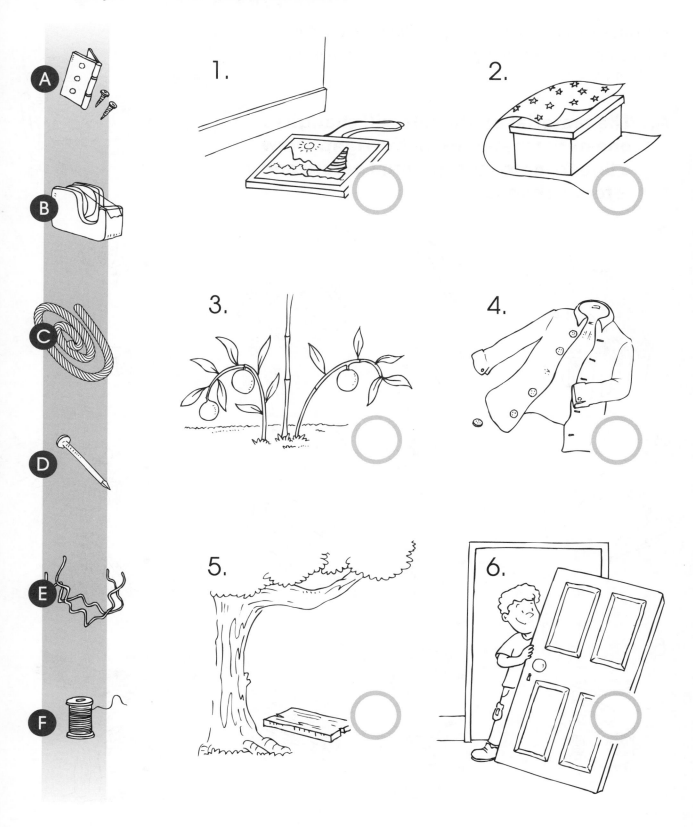

Changing Materials

- Heat, cold, and other things can change materials.
- When a material changes, some of its properties change.

A. **The material on the left will change to one of the materials on the right. Draw a line to match the material before and after its change.**

1.

2.

3.

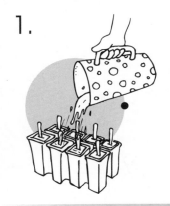

4.

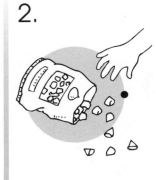

5.

6.

ISBN: 978-1-897164-29-7

B. Read what Dr. Stein says. Help him check ✔ the correct letters and fill in the blanks.

thick   liquid
sticky   soft
fluffy   wet

Look at the change in each material. Tell whether the second one feels, smells, tastes, or looks different from the first one. Then describe the new properties of each material.

Project 1

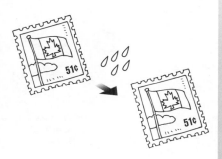

It ___ different.

Ⓐ feels

Ⓑ smells

Ⓒ tastes

Ⓓ looks

New properties:

_____

_____

Project 2

It ___ different.

Ⓐ feels

Ⓑ smells

Ⓒ tastes

Ⓓ looks

New properties:

_____

_____

Project 3

It ___ different.

Ⓐ feels

Ⓑ smells

Ⓒ tastes

Ⓓ looks

New properties:

_____

_____

ISBN: 978-1-897164-29-7

13

Reuse and Recycle

- Many objects may be reused or recycled.
- We sort objects for recycling by the materials they are made from.

A. **Put the objects into the correct recycle bins. Write the letters.**

 A

 B Jam

 C

 D

 E Yogurt

 F

 G PIZZA

 H

 I

 J

 K

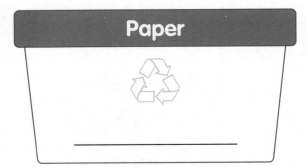
Paper

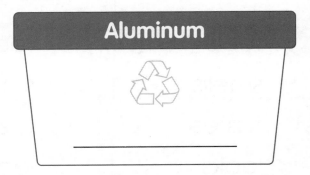
Aluminum

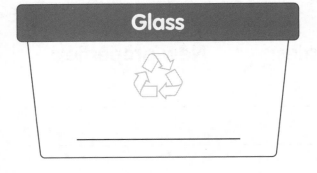
Glass

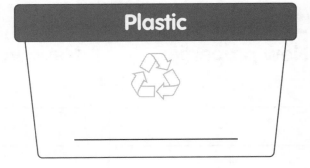
Plastic

ISBN: 978-1-897164-29-7

B. **Look at the picture. Colour the objects that are being reused or recycled.**

C. **How can each object be reused? Draw a picture.**

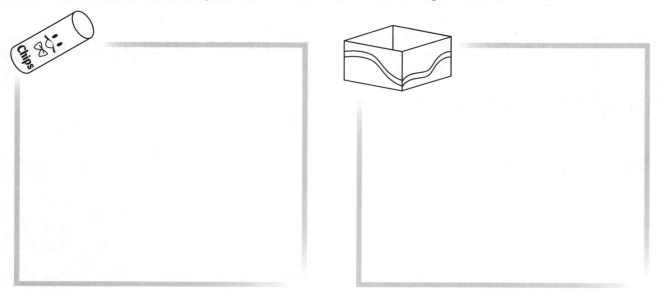

14

Energy and the Sun

- Energy makes things move or change.
- Most of the energy on Earth comes from the sun.

A. Help Sam write the words that the pictures stand for.

The 1._____ ☼ produces most of the energy

found on Earth. Energy is what makes 2._____

🚗 move. It makes 3._____ ⛵ sail. This

energy is used by 4._____ 🌳 to make their own

food. We get energy when we eat 5._____

🍗. Our 6._____ 👦👧 need energy to work

properly. Without the 7._____ ☼,

there would be no life

on 8._____ 🌍.

ISBN: 978-1-897164-29-7

B. Trace the dotted lines to complete the sun. Then colour the words related to the sun in the word search.

sun   life   energy
heat   light

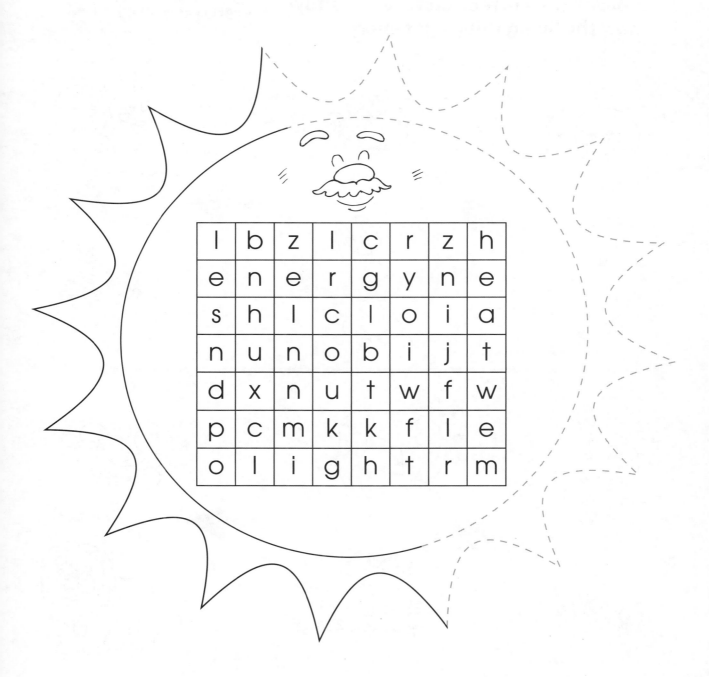

l	b	z	l	c	r	z	h
e	n	e	r	g	y	n	e
s	h	l	c	l	o	i	a
n	u	n	o	b	i	j	t
d	x	n	u	t	w	f	w
p	c	m	k	k	f	l	e
o	l	i	g	h	t	r	m

15

Energy and Food

- The sun provides energy for green plants and all other living things.
- We get energy to keep us active and alive by eating other living things.

I get energy from food.

A. **Colour the correct pictures to show how the living things get energy.**

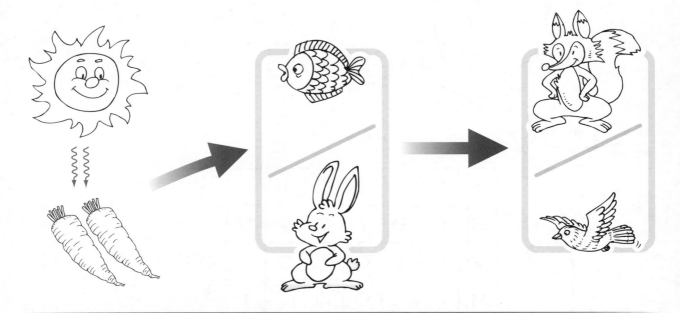

ISBN: 978-1-897164-29-7

B. **Complete the food chain with the given words.**

lion   grasshopper   fox   grass

Food chain:

☼ _____ ➡ _____ ➡ _____ ➡ _____

C. **We need energy to do things every day. Put in order the following things done from the least amount of energy used to the greatest. Write the letters.**

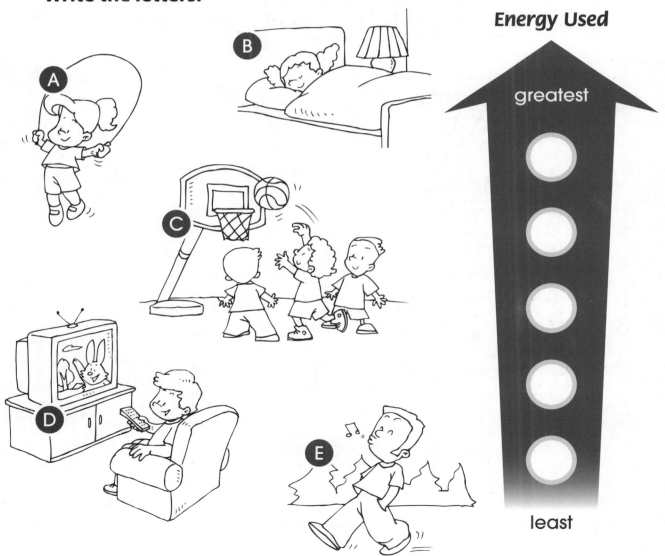

Smart Energy Use

- We use energy to make our lives easier.
- The energy we use comes from many different places.
- Our senses help us use energy wisely.

I like sports, but I want to save my energy.

A. Write the names of the energy givers in the pictures with the given words.

sun   electricity   wood   oil   wind

1. _____

2. _____

3. _____

4. _____

5. _____

ISBN: 978-1-897164-29-7

B. **What senses do we use to tell ourselves when we need energy, or when to stop using energy? Write the senses on the lines.**

hearing   sight   touch

1.

_____

2.

_____

3.

_____

C. **Colour the scene that shows the wiser use of energy in each pair.**

ISBN: 978-1-897164-29-7

17

Structure around Us

- Structures can be made to do things for us.
- Structures can be made from simple shapes.

A. Match the structures with their purposes. Write the letters.

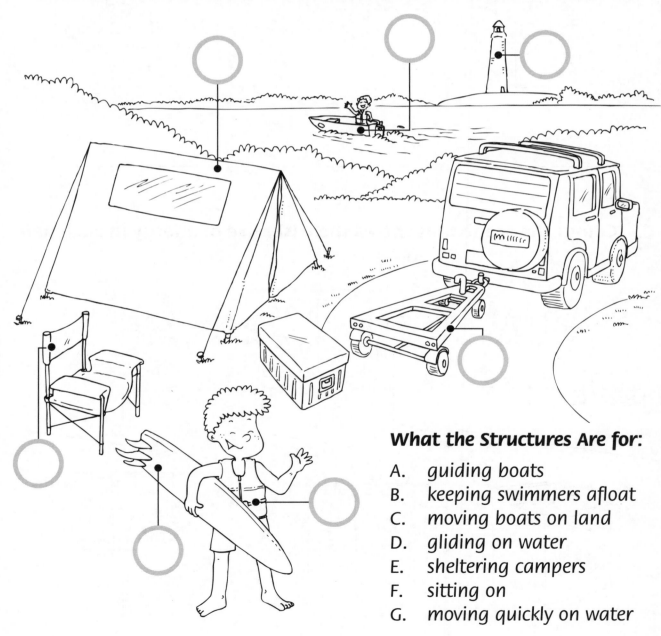

What the Structures Are for:

A. guiding boats
B. keeping swimmers afloat
C. moving boats on land
D. gliding on water
E. sheltering campers
F. sitting on
G. moving quickly on water

ISBN: 978-1-897164-29-7

B. Name and colour the shapes. Then find an example of each shape in the camping scene on page 346 by colouring it with the same colour.

Rectangle – yellow **Circle** – orange **Triangle** – blue

1. _____

2. _____

3. _____

C. Connect the dots and write the names of the structures.

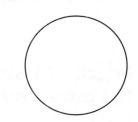

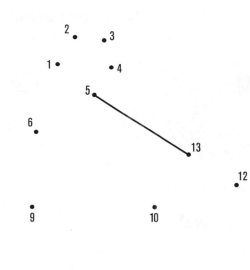

_____

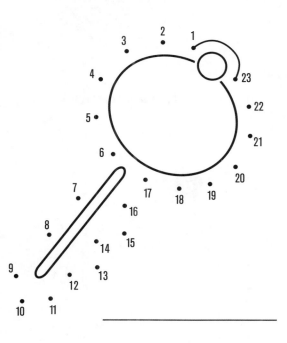

_____

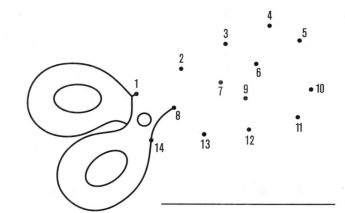

_____

ISBN: 978-1-897164-29-7

18

Natural Structures

- Living and non-living things produce structures.
- We see structures in the natural world and we create versions of our own based on them.

A. Match each structure with the correct builder. Write the letter.

A. spider   B. honeybee   C. robin   D. termite
E. woodpecker   F. freezing and thawing water

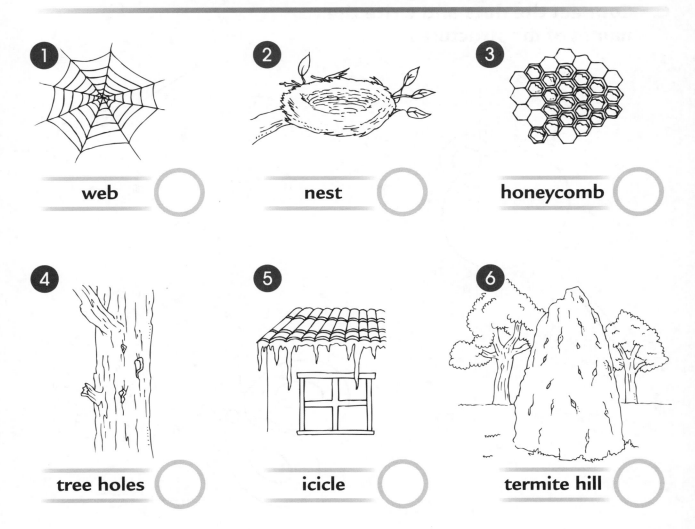

1 web ◯

2 nest ◯

3 honeycomb ◯

4 tree holes ◯

5 icicle ◯

6 termite hill ◯

ISBN: 978-1-897164-29-7

B. Write the names of the natural structures that are similar to the human constructions.

spider web   beaver dam   honeycomb

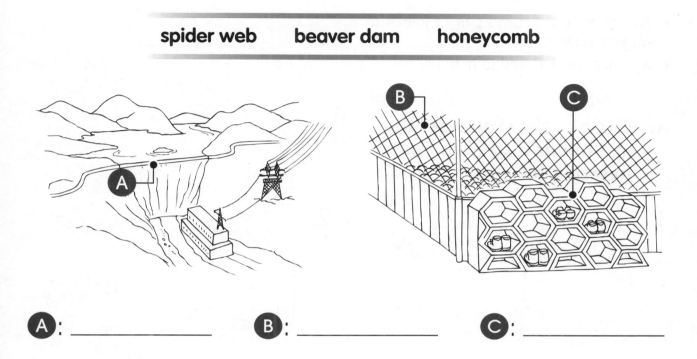

A: _____   B: _____   C: _____

C. Match the structures found in our body with the jobs that they perform.

Body Structures   Jobs They Do

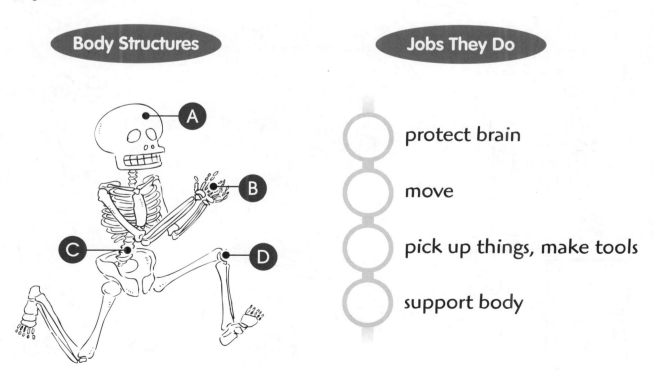

protect brain

move

pick up things, make tools

support body

ISBN: 978-1-897164-29-7

19

Structures Together

A lock and a box make a safe.

- Two or more structures can be joined to make a device.
- A device can be used to help us.

A. Circle ⬭ the structures that are needed to make each new device.

1.

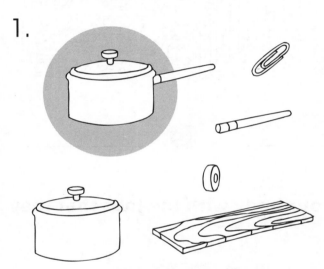

2.

3.

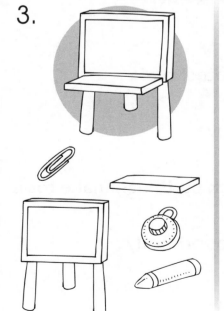

4.

5.

ISBN: 978-1-897164-29-7

B. Look at Gabe's new device. Check ✔ the correct pictures to show what structures Gabe has used to build it.

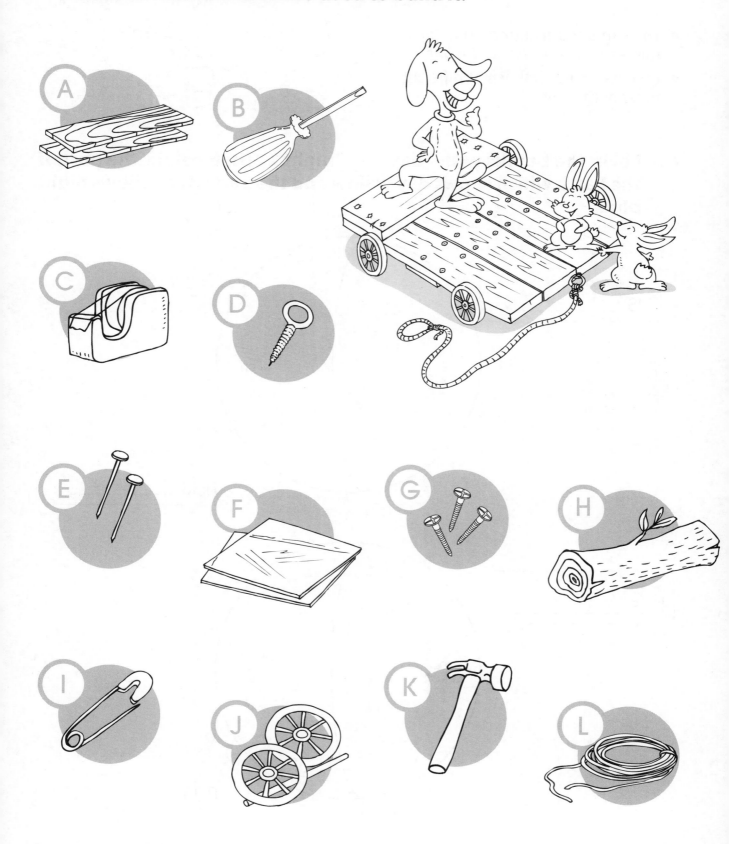

ISBN: 978-1-897164-29-7

20

Day and Night

- The sun gives us light. The Earth rotates to give us day and night.
- Different things happen at different times of the day.

A. Fill in the blanks with "day" or "night". Then colour the part of the Earth which shows day yellow and the part which shows night blue.

1.

It is _____ .

It is _____ .

2.

It is _____ .

It is _____ .

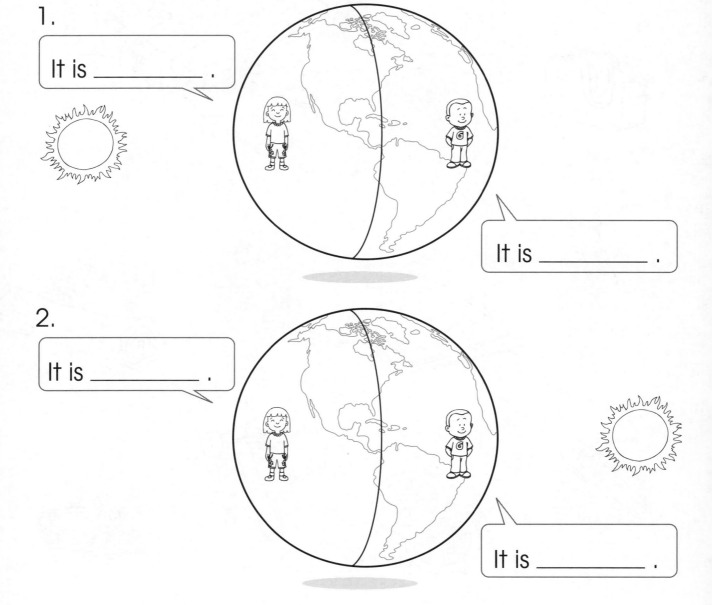

ISBN: 978-1-897164-29-7

B.   Check ✔ the picture that happens next.

1.   A sunflower following the sun, shown at three different times of a day:

2.   A child's daily routine:

C.   Match the shadows with the times of a day.   Write the letters.

21

Seasons

- The four seasons are spring, summer, fall, and winter.
- The things we do depend on the season we are in.

A. **When do we do these activities? Put them in the correct groups. Write the letters.**

Work

Play

  Summer

Work: _____

Play: _____

 **Winter**

Work: _____

Play: _____

   ISBN: 978-1-897164-29-7

B. Fill in the missing letters to complete the name of each season. Then colour the picture that matches the season.

1.

s__ri__ __

2.

su__ __e__

3.

__al__

4.

w__ __t__r

C. Answer the questions.

What season is it now?

_____

What do you like to do in summer?

_____

ISBN: 978-1-897164-29-7

22

Plants through the Seasons

- *From season to season, we can see changes in many plants.*

A. Write the correct season for each picture.

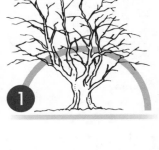

1. _____

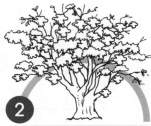

2. _____

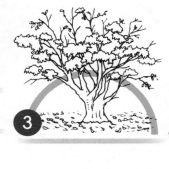

3. _____

4. _____

B. Colour the maple leaves in different seasons.

1. Summer

2. Fall

ISBN: 978-1-897164-29-7

C. **Draw lines to match the plants in spring with the same plant in summer.**

In Spring

In Summer

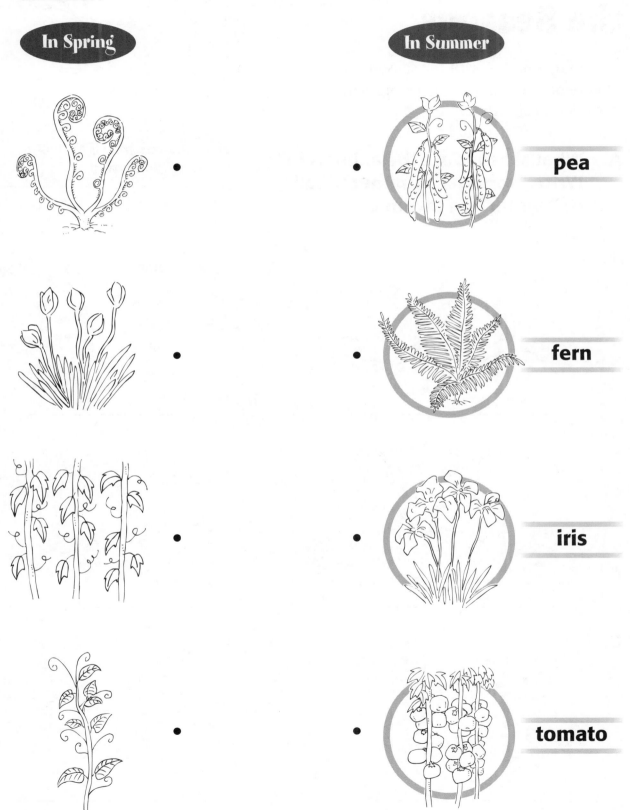

pea

fern

iris

tomato

ISBN: 978-1-897164-29-7

23

Animals through the Seasons

- Animals change with the seasons.
- Animals have different ways of living through cold winters.

> I will dress myself in thick coat for the whole winter.

A. **What seasons are the animals in? Write "spring", "summer", "fall", or "winter" on the lines.**

1.

_____

2.

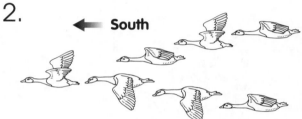

← **South**

_____

3.

_____

4.

_____

5.

_____

6.

_____

ISBN: 978-1-897164-29-7

B. **See what the animals do to live through cold winters. Match the pictures with the descriptions. Write the letters.**

Ⓐ **hibernate through cold winters**

Ⓑ **migrate to warm homes in the south**

Ⓒ **grow thick fur coats to help them stay warm**

C. **Read the poem. Write the season the animals are getting ready for.**

Store your nuts, young squirrel.

Go to sleep, little snail.

Eat your salmon, black bear.

Go south, humpback whale.

Night Animals

- Some animals sleep in the day, and hunt and eat at night. They are nocturnal.
- Nocturnal animals have strong senses that help them live in the dark.

A. Colour the nocturnal animals. Then match the animals with their names. Write the letters beside them.

A. raccoon
B. firefly
C. skunk
D. cat
E. bat
F. owl
G. toad
H. grizzly bear

ISBN: 978-1-897164-29-7

B. **Match the strong senses with the correct nocturnal animals.**
Circle ◯ the correct animals.

1. **Sense of Hearing**

2. **Sense of Sight**

3. **Sense of Smell**

4. **Sense of Touch**

ISBN: 978-1-897164-29-7

A. Write the name of each organ. Then tell what sense each organ has.

eye   nose   tongue
ear   skin

touch   taste   smell
hearing   sight

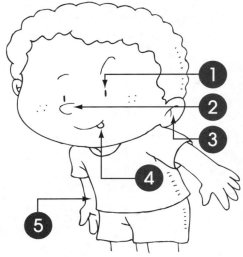

1. _____ ; sense of _____

2. _____ ; sense of _____

3. _____ ; sense of _____

4. _____ ; sense of _____

5. _____ ; sense of _____

B. Tell the three things that living things need. Circle ○ the correct words. Then write the letters in the correct places.

Living Things Need

- Air / Fur:

  ___ , ___

- Water / Sea:

  ___ , ___

- Fruit / Food:

  ___ , ___

ISBN: 978-1-897164-29-7

C. Match the pictures with the correct descriptions. Write the letters.

1. Living things: _____

2. Living things with patterns: _____

3. Healthy food: _____

4. Things that can protect our organs: _____

5. Things made of metal: _____

6. Things made of wood: _____

ISBN: 978-1-897164-29-7

D. Each material has gone through a change. Colour the correct picture that shows the material after its change.

1.

2.

3.

4.

E. Draw lines to put the objects into the correct recycle bins.

| Paper | Aluminum | Glass | Plastic |

ISBN: 978-1-897164-29-7

F. **Match the structures with their purposes. Write the letters. Then answer the questions.**

1. What the structures are for:

> **A. linking to the world**   **B. sitting on**
>
> **C. giving knowledge**   **D. writing**
>
> **E. ventilation**   **F. writing on**

2. Name a structure in the picture that has the shape

   a. of a rectangle. _____

   b. of a circle. _____

ISBN: 978-1-897164-29-7

G. Write "day" or "night" in the boxes. Then colour the part of the Earth which shows day yellow and the part which shows night blue.

1.

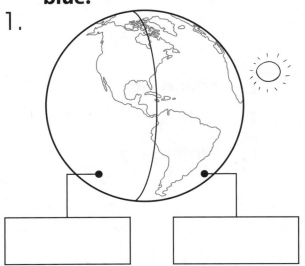

2.

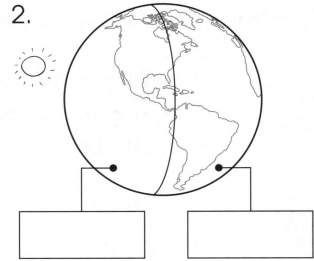

H. Cross out ✗ the picture that does not belong in each group. Then name the season that the pictures show.

1.

2.

3.

4.

ISBN: 978-1-897164-29-7

I. Colour the correct pictures.

1. Nocturnal animals

2. Nocturnal animals that have good sight

3. Animals that hibernate through cold winter

4. Structures built by animals

ISBN: 978-1-897164-29-7

ISBN: 978-1-897164-29-7

ANSWERS

ISBN: 978-1-897164-29-7

1 Comparison

1.

2.

3.

4.

5.

6.

7. A   8. A
9. B   10. A
11. B   12. A

13.

14.

15.

16.

17. B, C, A   18. B, A, C
19. C, A, B   20. B, C, A
21. C, A, B ;
     A, C, B

22. (Suggested answer for the longer bracelet)

23. same   24. bigger
25. biggest   26. longer
27. shorter   28. shorter

2 More about Comparison

1.

2.

3.

4.
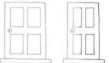

5.

6.
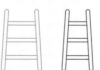

7.

8.

9.

10.

11.

ISBN: 978-1-897164-29-7

12.

13. B

14. C

15. B

16.

17.

18.

19.

20.

21.

22. heavier

23. lighter

24.

25.

26.

27.

28.

29. A

30. B

31. A

3   Ordering and Sorting

1. ✔

2.

3. ✔

4. ✔

5.

6. B ; A ; D ; C

7. A ; D ; B ; C

8. B ; C ; D ; A

9. A ; D ; C ; B

10.

11.

12.

13.

14.

15. Animals: B, C ;
    Plants: A, D, E

16. Food: A, C, D ;
    Toy: B, E

4   Sequencing

1. B ; C ; A

2. A ; C ; B

3. A ; B ; C

4. B ; C ; A

5. A ; D ; B ; C ;

6. C ; B ; D ; A ;

7. A ; C ; B ; D ;

8. 1st ; ; yellow

9. ; 5th

10. ; 5th

11. ; 2nd

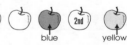

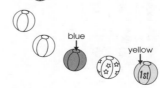

ISBN: 978-1-897164-29-7

12. fifth
13. seventh
14. second
15. eighth
16. first
17. fourth
18. fourth ; third
19. first ; fourth ; sixth

5 Numbers 1 to 10

1. 3
2. 5
3. 6
4. 8
5. 2
6. 9
7. five
8. seven
9. six
10. eight
11. three
12. nine
13. 6
14. 10
15. 3
16. 8
17. 3
18. 6
19. ; 4
20. ; 6
21. ; 5
22. ; 9
23.
24.
25.
26.
27. 3 ; 4
28. 6 ; 7
29. 5 ; 4
30. 8 ; 7
31. 6 ; 7 ; 8
32. 7 ; 6 ; 4
33. 7 ;

5	6	7	8

34. 3 ;

3	4	5	6

35. 3 ;

2	3	4	5

36. 9 ;

6	7	8	9

6 Addition and Subtraction of 1

1. 5 ; ; 6
2. 6 ; ; 7
3. 3 ; ; 4
4. 2 ; ; 3
5. ; 5 ; 1 ; 6
6. ; 4 ; 1 ; 5
7. ; 3 ; 1 ; 4
8. ; 1 ; 6 ; 7
9. 7 ; ; 6
10. 6 ; ; 5
11. 3 ; ; 2
12. 9 ; ; 8
13. 8 ; ; 7
14. ; 6 ; 1 ; 5
15. ; 6 ; 1 ; 5

ISBN: 978-1-897164-29-7

16. 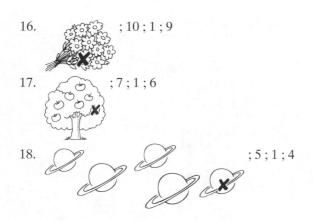 ; 10 ; 1 ; 9

17. ; 7 ; 1 ; 6

18. ; 5 ; 1 ; 4

18. 4 ; 1 ; 3
19. 5 ; 2 ; 3
20. 2 ; 3 ; 5
21. 2 ; 4 ; 6 ; 6
22. 3 ; 1 ; 2 ; 2

7 Addition and Subtraction Facts to 6

1. ☼ ☼ ; 2 ; 5

2. ☺ ☺ ; 2 ; 4

3. ; 1 ; 5

4. ; 3 ; 6

5. 2 ; 4
6. 4 ; 1 ; 5
7. 2 ; 1 ; 3
8. 3 ; 2 ; 5
9. 3 ; 1 ; 4
10. 2 ; 3 ; 5

11-12. (Individual drawings)
11. 6
12. 6

13. ; 1 ; 2 ; 1 ; 2

14.  ; 2 ; 2 ; 2 ; 2

15. ; 3 ; 4 ; 3 ; 4

16.  ; 1 ; 8 ; 1 ; 8

17. 3 ; 1 ; 4

8 Addition and Subtraction Facts to 10

1. 5 ; 9   2. 5 ; 2 ; 7
3. 6 ; 3 ; 9   4. 2 ; 6 ; 8
5. 5 ; 2 ; 7   6. 4 ; 4 ; 8
7. 8   8. 6
9. 7   10. 10
11. 7   12. 9
13. 9   14. 5

15-24. (Draw 10 apples in the tree.)
15. 9   16. 4
17. 8   18. 8
19. 7   20. 10
21. 6   22. 6
23. 8   24. 7
25. 6 ; 2 ; 4   26. 5 ; 3 ; 2
27. 6 ; 5 ; 1   28. 9 ; 3 ; 6
29. 7 ; 3 ; 4   30. 8 ; 5 ; 3
31. 5   32. 3
33. 5   34. 2
35. 7   36. 4
37. 6   38. 4
39. 8   40. 3
41. 3   42. 8
43. 4   44. 10
45. 4   46. 9
47. 4
48.  ; 4

9 More about Addition and Subtraction

1. 7   2. 8
3. 7   4. 4
5. 1   6. 3
7. 8   8. 3
9. 7   10. 2
11. 9   12. 7
13. 5   14. 5

ISBN: 978-1-897164-29-7

15. 9   16. 2
17. 6   18. 5 ; 5
19. 7   20. 0 ; 3
21. 0 ; 4   22. 0 ; 5
23. 9   24. 8
25. 6   26. 1
27. 5   28. 4
29. 7   30. 3
31. 2   32. 0
33. 0   34. 0
35. 0   36. 0
37. 0   38. 0
39. 0   40. 0
41. 2 − 2 = 0 ; 0
42. 5 − 5 = 0 ; 0
43. 5 + 2 = 7 ; 7
44. 7 − 3 = 4 ; 4
45. 4 + 4 = 8 ; 8
46. 5 − 5 = 0 ; 0

10 Numbers 1 to 20

1. 6   2. 8
3. 16   4. 14
5. 15   6. 12
7. 16   8. 13
9. 20   10. 14
11. 11   12. 17
13. 8   14. 16
15. 11   16. 15
17. 9   18. 4
19. 14 ; 15 ; 16 ; 18
20. 17 ; 16 ; 14 ; 13
21. 9 ; 10 ; 12 ; 13
22. 7 ; 6 ; 4 ; 3
23. 12 ; 13 ; 14 ; 16
24. 14 ; 13 ; 12 ; 10
25. 5, 9, 13
26. 2, 10, 16
27. 4, 5, 8, 10
28. 2, 3, 7, 11
29. 12 ;
30. 15 ;

31. 8 ;
32. ; odd
32. ; even
33.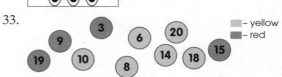

11 Numbers 21 to 100

1. 48   2. 37
3. 53   4. 66
5.

1	2	3	4	5	6	7	8	9	10
11	12	13	14	15	16	17	18	19	20
21	22	23	24	25	26	27	28	29	30
31	32	33	34	35	36	37	38	39	40
41	42	43	44	45	46	47	48	49	50
51	52	53	54	55	56	57	58	59	60
61	62	63	64	65	66	67	68	69	70
71	72	73	74	75	76	77	78	79	80
81	82	83	84	85	86	87	88	89	90
91	92	93	94	95	96	97	98	99	100

6. 57   7. 73
8. 90   9. 93
10. 66   11. 39
12. 66 ; 67 ; 70 ; 71
13. 90 ; 92 ; 93 ; 95
14. 42 ; 40 ; 39 ; 38
15. Tens 4 Ones 7 ; 4 ; 7 ; 40 ; 7
16. Tens 5 Ones 2 ; 5 ; 2 ; 50 ; 2
17. 6 ; 5   18. 10
19. 3 ; 8   20. 6
21. 9 ; 7   22. 80 ; 7
23. 53   24. 34
25. 49   26. 61
27. 54   28. 85
29. 23

ISBN: 978-1-897164-29-7

30. 88 ;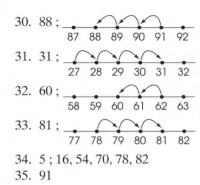

31. 31 ;

32. 60 ;

33. 81 ;

34. 5 ; 16, 54, 70, 78, 82

35. 91

12 Counting by 1's, 2's, 5's, or 10's

1. 87 ; 88 ; 90 ; 91 ; 92
2. 10 ; 9 ; 7 ; 6 ; 4
3. 17 ; 15 ; 14 ; 12 ; 11
4. 66 ; 67 ; 69 ; 70 ; 71
5. 47, 48, 49, 50, 51, 52, 53, 54, 55, 56, 57, 58
6. 16, 15, 14, 13, 12, 11, 10, 9, 8, 7, 6
7.

   2 ; 4 ; 6 ; 8 ; 10 ; 12 ; 14 ; 16 ; 16
8.

   2, 4, 6, 8, 10, 12, 14 ; 14
9.

   2, 4, 6, 8, 10, 12, 14, 16, 18 ; 18
10. 6
11. 8
12. 18
13. 16
14. 80 ; 82 ; 84 ; 88
15. 30 ; 28 ; 24 ; 22
16. a. 5   b. 10
    c. 15   d. 20
    e. 25   f. 30
    g. 35   h. 40
    i. 45   j. 50
17. 35 ; 45 ; 50 ; 60
18. 70 ; 75 ; 85 ; 95
19. 70 ; 65 ; 60 ; 50
20. 20 ; 25 ; 35 ; 40
21.   ; 60

22. 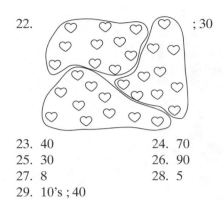   ; 30

23. 40   24. 70
25. 30   26. 90
27. 8   28. 5
29. 10's ; 40

13 Money

1.

   Toonie ; $ 2
   Lonnie ; $ 1
   Quarter ; 25 ¢
   Dime ; 10 ¢
   Nickel ; 5 ¢
   Penny ; 1 ¢

2. toonie   3. dime
4.   5.
6.   7.
8.   9.
10. C, A, B
11. B, C, A
12. B, C, A
13. A, C, B
14. 17   15. 14
16. 18   17. 8
18. 16   19. 14
20.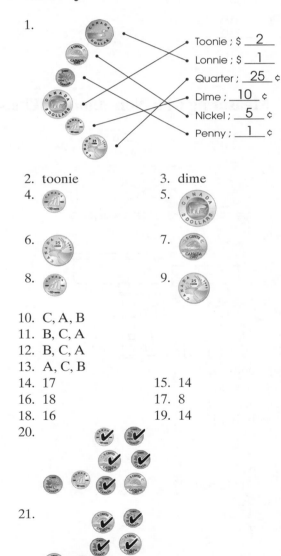

21.

ISBN: 978-1-897164-29-7

22.

23.

24.   4¢ ; 9
    + 5¢
    ─────
      9¢

25.   8¢ ; 5
    − 3¢
    ─────
      5¢

26.   10¢ ; 2
    − 8¢
    ─────
      2¢

14 Measuring with Non-standard Units

1. 5 ; 15   2. 6 ; 18
3. 3 ; 9   4. 1 ; 3
5.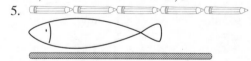

6.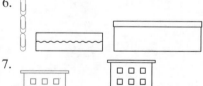

7.

8. belts
9. straws
10. a. 6 ; 10
    b. 10 ; 15
11.
12. 6 ; 10
13. 40 ; 12 ; 30 ; 32
14.
15. 2

16.  ; 33

Review 1

1.
2.
3. B, A, C
4. A, C, B
5. 9 ; nine
6. 4 ; four
7. 53, 49, 24, 14
8. 90, 84, 48, 9
9. 77, 71, 70, 17
10. ; 32

11. ; 30

12. ; 45

13. a. 4
    b-c.

14. 11   15. 4
16. 9   17. 11
18. 7   19. 12
20. 5   21. 8
22. 13   23. 11

ISBN: 978-1-897164-29-7

24. 6   25. 7
26. 4 + 9 ; 13 ; 13
27. 8 + 9 ; 17 ; 17
28. 15 – 4 ; 11 ; 11
29. 15 – 8 ; 7 ; 7
30. have
31. 2 ; 1 ;
    2 quarters and 1 nickel ;
    1 toonie and 3 loonies
32. Lucy and Paul
33. 25
34. 4
35. $\boxed{10}$; 4
    $\ominus$ $\boxed{6}$
    $\boxed{4}$
36. a. 8   b. 16
    c. $\square$
37. a. 36   b. 32
    c.
38. a. A   b. B

15 Capacity

1.

2.

3.

4.

5.

6.

7.

8. a. more   b. the same capacity
9. a. less   b.
10. a. 7 ; 9   b. 2
11. a. 6   b. 1 ; 3
    c. more   d. 9
12. B   13. A
14. A   15. B
16. 8

16 Mass

1.   2.

3. 1 ; 2 ; 3
4. 2 ; 3 ; 1
5. 1 ; 3 ; 2
6.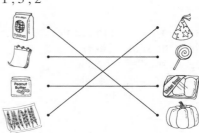

7. a. heavier
   b. lighter
8. a. heavier
   b. lighter
9. a. 10   b. 8
   c. 7   d. 5
10. house
11. doll
12.

13. 8   14. 4
15. 12   16. 2
17. 1 ; 1
18.

17 2-D Shapes

1.
   Circle
   Hexagon
   Pentagon
   Rectangle
   Square
   Triangle

2.  ; triangle

3. ; hexagon

4. ; rectangle

5. narrower ; wider ; the same
6. taller ; the same ; shorter
7. bigger ; smaller ; the same
8.   a. triangle
           b. 3 ; 3

9.   a. hexagon
           b. 6 ; 6

10.   a. pentagon
           b. 5 ; 5

11.   a. rectangle
           b. 4 ; 4

12.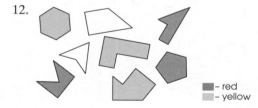

■ – red
■ – yellow

13. (Suggested drawing)

18 More about Shapes

1.

triangle, pentagon

2.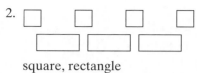

square, rectangle

3.

hexagon, circle

4.

triangle, circle

5.

6.

7.  ; one

8.  ; one

9.  ; one

10. 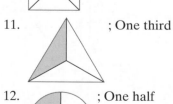 ; one fourth

11. ; One third

12. ; One half

ISBN: 978-1-897164-29-7

13. a. one fourth
    b. three fourths
14. a. one half
    b. one half
15. a. two thirds
    b. one third
16. No, because the sword is not in four equal parts.

19 3-D Solids

1.
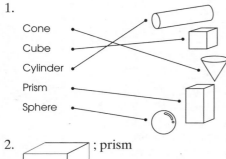

2.  ; prism

3. ; cylinder

4-9. (Individual drawings)
   4. cone   5. sphere
   6. prism   7. cylinder
   8. cube   9. cone
10. ; circle

11. ; circle

12. ; square

13. ; rectangle

14. ; rectangle

15. sphere ; except that it is flat at the top and the bottom.
16. cylinder ; except that it goes thinner at the bottom.
17. cube ; except that it has four short legs at the bottom.
18.

20 Directions (1)

1. Eric   2. Bill
3. in front of   4. behind
5. 2   6. 2
7. a. C   b. in front of
   c. behind
8. a. B   b. in front of
   c. in front of
9. a. right   b. left
   c. right
10. a. left   b. left
    c. left
11.

12. Cindy ; Mabel ; Tammy ; Sue
13. in front of
14. behind
15. left
16. right
17. behind
18. right
19. left

21 Directions (2)

1. a. inside   b. outside
2. a. outside   b. inside
3. a. inside   b. outside
4. a. under   b. over
   c. under   d. under
   e. under   f. over
   g-h.

5. Colour picture C. ; under
6. Colour picture A. ; over
7. Colour picture B. ; inside

ISBN: 978-1-897164-29-7

8. inside
9. over
10. over
11. over
12. inside
13. There are 4 stars over the head of the clown.
14. The mouse is inside the hole.

22 Temperatures

1. Spring: B, G
   Summer: D, F
   Fall: C, E
   Winter: A, H
2. a. winter ; 4
   b. spring ; 1
   c. fall ; 3
   d. summer ; 2
3. ; sunny ; warm ;

   ; sunny ; hottest ;

   ; cold ;

   ; snowy ; coldest
4. low ; B
5. high ; hotter ; A
6. getting warmer
7. getting colder
8. 16 ; mild
9. 8 ; cold
10. 30 ; hot
11. 2 ; cold
12. 27 ;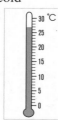

23 Days, Weeks, Months, and Time

1. Wednesday
2. Sunday ; Saturday
3. 3
4. Friday

5. playing with computer
6. 7
7. 5 ; 9 ; 7 ;
   6 ; 10 ; 2 ;
   3 ; 12 ; 1 ;
   4 ; 11 ; 8
8.

| OCTOBER | | | | | | |
SUN	MON	TUE	WED	THU	FRI	SAT
	1	2	3	(4)	5	6
7	8	9	10	11	12	13
	15	16	17	18	19	20
21	22	23	24	25	26	27
28	29	30				

○ Field Trip

9. Monday
10. Oct 4th
11. Oct 14th
12. Oct 29th
13. A: 7 ; 7
    B: 2 o'clock ; 2:00
    C: 9 o'clock ; 9:00
    D: 10 o'clock ; 10:00
14. A ; C ; B ; D
15. nearly ; 9 ; a little after 4 o'clock ; a little after half past 11
16.
17.
18.
19.
20.
21.
22.

24 Patterns

1. ✔
2. ✗
3. ✔
4. ✗
5. ✔

ISBN: 978-1-897164-29-7

6.

7.

8.

9.

10.

11.

12.

13-14. (Individual designs)

13.

14.

15.

16.

1	2	3	4	5	6	7	8	9	10
11	12	13	14	15	16	17	18	19	20
21	22	23	24	25	26	27	28	29	30
31	32	33	34	35	36	37	38	39	40
41	42	43	44	45	46	47	48	49	50
51	52	53	54	55	56	57	58	59	60
61	62	63	64	65	66	67	68	69	70
71	72	73	74	75	76	77	78	79	80
81	82	83	84	85	86	87	88	89	90
91	92	93	94	95	96	97	98	99	100

17. There is a 5 in the ones place.

25 Organizing Data

1. A: Apple: 15
    Orange: 20
   B: Big: 18
    Small: 17
2. A: Plant: ||||| ||
   B: Circle: ||||| |||||
    Square: ||||| ||||

3.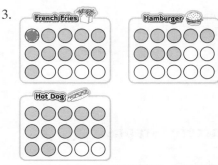

4.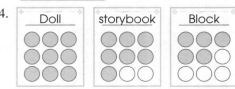

| Doll | storybook | Block |

5. dolls

26 Pictographs

1. fewer   2. fewer
3. 3   4. 4
5. 5   6. 4
7. 3   8. 2
9. basketball   10. 3
11. skating
12.

Children's Stickers

| Mark | Judy | George | Susan |

13. Mark
14. Judy
15. 2
16.

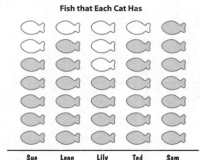

Fish that Each Cat Has

| Sue | Leon | Lily | Ted | Sam |

ISBN: 978-1-897164-29-7

17. Sam
18. Lily
19. 12
20. 28
21. 19

27 Concrete Graphs

1. 3 ; 4 ; 5 ; 5
2. 4
3. 2
4. 9
5. 15
6. a. 4
   b. 5
7. 3
8. 3
9. by school bus
10. by bike
11.

Drinks that the Children Want

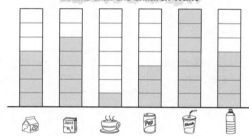

12. a. 5
    b. 4
13. 24
14. In summer, because almost all the children wanted cold drinks.
15.

Combos to Be Ordered

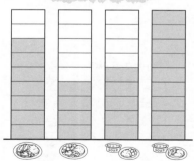

16. 5
17. D
18. 25
19. 16 combos

28 Probability

1.   2.

3.   4.

5. a. certain
   b. impossible
6. a. impossible
   b. certain
7. a. impossible
   b. certain
8. a. certain
   b. impossible
9-14. (Suggested answers)
9. impossible
10. likely
11. certain
12. unlikely
13. likely
14. certain
15. a. less
    b. more
16. a. less
    b. more
17.

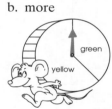

Review 2

1.

2.

3. 6 ; 4 ; 5 ; 8
4. D
5. B

ISBN: 978-1-897164-29-7

6. 10

7.  ; hexagon ; 6 ; 6

8.  ; rectangle ; 4 ; 4

9. 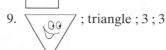 ; triangle ; 3 ; 3

10.  ; pentagon ; 5 ; 5

11.

12. A: prism
    B: cube
    C: cone
    D: sphere
13. under
14. behind
15. left
16. in front of
17. inside
18.

19. summer ; 28
20. fall ; 14
21. spring ; 20
22. winter ; 0
23. Friday ; Saturday
24. Sunday
25. swimming (lesson)

26. 4

27.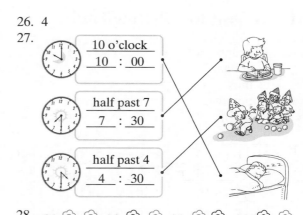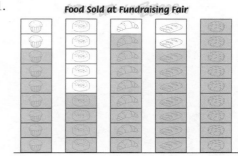

28.

29.

30.

31.
Food Sold at Fundraising Fair

32. 5
33. Cookie
34. 35
35. impossible
36. likely

ISBN: 978-1-897164-29-7

1   A Visit to a Petting Farm

A. 1. countryside
    2. animals
    3. milk
    4. ponies
    5. patch
    6. sweet

B.

b	h	k	l	e	n	q	i	a	o	u	m	d
p	a	n	i	m	a	l	s	v	l	p	i	c
d	i	s	n	w	z	p	y	g	x	o	l	q
k	c	z	b	j	v	a	h	o	w	n	k	m
g	t	c	o	u	n	t	r	y	s	i	d	e
n	p	m	g	y	j	c	w	e	r	e	i	k
f	a	r	o	u	x	h	l	j	p	s	t	h
e	h	i	c	s	w	e	e	t	d	m	b	f

C. 1. p
    2. f
    3. s
    4. b
    5. w
    6. h

D. 1. g
    2. d
    3. b
    4. c
    5. t
    6. p
    7. r
    8. p

2   Over the Ocean Blue

A. 1. sailboat
    2. ocean liner
    3. kayak
    4. canoe

B. 1. ✔
    2.
    3. ✔
    4.
    5. ✔
    6. ✔

C. 1.

    2.

    3.

D.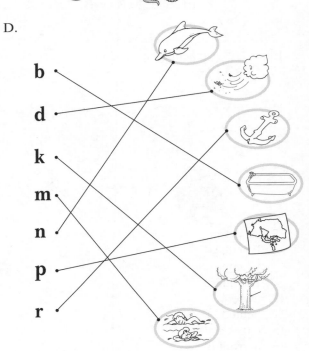

3   The Story of the Greedy Dog

A. 1. sad
    2. wide
    3. new
    4. opened
    5. big
    6. take

B. 1. No
    2. Yes
    3. Yes
    4. No
    5. Yes

ISBN: 978-1-897164-29-7

C.

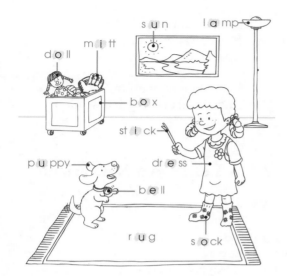

d**o**ll   m**i**tt   s**u**n   l**a**mp   b**o**x   st**i**ck   p**u**ppy   dr**e**ss   b**e**ll   r**u**g   s**o**ck

D. 1.

tap / pat ; hat

2.

pet ; jet ; pen

3.

big ; bib ; him

4.

mop ; dog / god ; fox

5.

sun ; cup ; bug

6.

bit ; bag ; hut

4   Sometimes We Just Like to Look at the Sky...

A. 1. ☁
    2. ☁
    3. ☁
    4. ☁
    5. ☁
    6. ☁

B. (Individual drawing and writing)

C. 1. a ; a ; a ; a
    2. o ; o ; o ; o ; o
    3. u ; u ; u ; u
    4. i ; i ; i ; i

D.

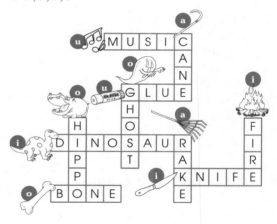

5   Variety – the Spice of Life

A. Food: sushi ; dim sum ; stew ; apple pie
    Taste: sour ; salty ; sweet ; spicy

B. (Suggested answers)
    1-syllable word: eat
    2-syllable word: apple
    3-syllable word: cucumber
    4-syllable word: jambalaya

ISBN: 978-1-897164-29-7

C.

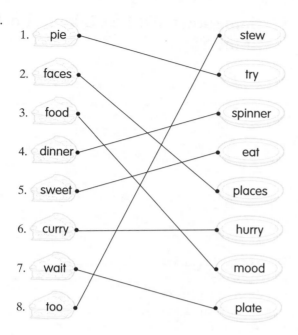

D. (Colour these words.)
1. thicken
2. bushy
3. meat
4. handle
5. good
6. bees

6 A Chant from Ghana

A. 3 ; 5 ; 1 ; 2 ; 4
B. (Individual writing and drawing)
C.

D. 1. girl ; pool
2. fish ; water
3. weather
4. sun ; sky
5. children ; schoolyard
E. (Individual drawing and writing)

7 A Letter to a New Friend

A. 1. Choco
2. Emi
3. Greg
4. Hugh
5. Kiyoka
6. Mandy
7. Sammy
B. 1. Sammy
2. Japan
3. pen pal
4. Samantha
5. Emi
C.

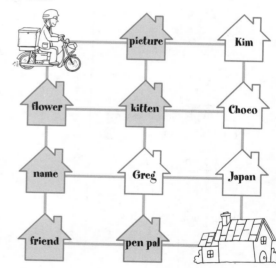

D. Person: brother ; cousin ; teacher
Animal: dog ; bird ; horse
Place: school ; farm ; park
Thing: letter ; picture ; cap

ISBN: 978-1-897164-29-7

8 A Letter from Japan

A. 1. Hana
   2. Kiyoka
   3. Kenichi
   4. Keiko
   5. Pekko
B. 1.
   2. ✔
   3.
   4. ✔
   5. ✔
C. 1. Sammy ; Canada
   2. Miss Wilson ; Kiyoka ; English
   3. Japan
   4. Japanese
   5. The Lion King
   6. Simba
   7. Lakeside School
   8. Toronto
   9. Pekko
D. (Answers will vary.)
   1. Jose likes playing with me.
   2. I feed Puffy every morning.
   3. My cousin works in Barrie.
   4. He is reading The Brave Heart.
   5. Miss Wilson is the best teacher in my school.
   6. Ottawa is a nice place to visit.

9 Our Chores

A. 6 ; 3 ; 5 ; 2 ; 1 ; 4
B. (Individual drawing and writing)
C. 1. beds
   2. flower
   3. school
   4. plants
   5. houses
   6. mug
   7. bowls
   8. book
   9. parents
D. 1. mop
   2. towel
   3. sink
   4. plates
   5. cups

6. balls
7. apples
8. cat
9. boy

10 Mr. Mom

A. 2 ; 1 ; 5 ; 3 ; 4
B. (Individual drawing and answer)
C. 1.
   2.
   3.
   4.
   5.
   6.
   7.
   8.
   9.
   10.
   11.
   12.
D. 1. C
   2. B
   3. E
   4. D
   5. A
E. (Individual writing)

11 Perogies

A.

ISBN: 978-1-897164-29-7

B. 1. Many
    2. fill
    3. like / love
    4. great
C. 1. ✔
    2. ✔
    3.
    4. ✔
    5.
    6.
D. 1. I like perogies.
    2. Tony loves toast with jam.
    3. Ice cream is Kim's favourite.
    4. We all enjoy eating.
E. (Individual drawing and writing)

12 The Sun and the Wind

A. 1. r ; heavy
    2. i ; strong
    3. k ; smiled
    4. e ; bright
    5. p ; forehead
B. 1. park
    2. heavy coat
    3. hard
    4. handkerchief
C. 1. No
    2. Yes
    3. Yes
    4. No
    5. Yes
    6. No
    7. Yes
D. 1. Is it cold in the fall?
    2. Do you like fluffy snow?
    3. Why is the winter so long?
    4. Who likes snowy days?
    5. What can we do in winter?
    6. When will the snow stop?
E. 1. Is it windy outside?
    2. Do you have a thicker coat?
    3. Where are you going?
    4. Are you coming with me?

13 Duck Hunting

A. 1. A
    2. B
    3. A
    4. A
    5. B
B. (Individual writing)
C. 1.
    2.
    3.
    4.
    5.
    6.
    7.
    8.
D. Bad luck!
E. 1. What a narrow escape!
    2. Dear me!
    3. You won't believe it!
    4. How bad the hunters are!

14 I Like Winter

A. 1. fall
    2. spring
    3. winter
    4. summer
B. (Individual writing)
C. 1. canada ; Canada
    2. algonquin park ; Algonquin Park
    3. kathleen ; Kathleen
    4. albert ; Albert
    5. ottawa ; Ottawa
    6. windsor hotel ; Windsor Hotel
    7. oscar ; Oscar

ISBN: 978-1-897164-29-7

D. 1. ✘ ; My sister and I like playing in snow.
   2. ✔
   3. ✘ ; Cindy names every snowman we build.
   4. ✘ ; The biggest one is called Starlie.
   5. ✘ ; I like Witty, the smallest one, best.
   6. ✔

Review 1

A.

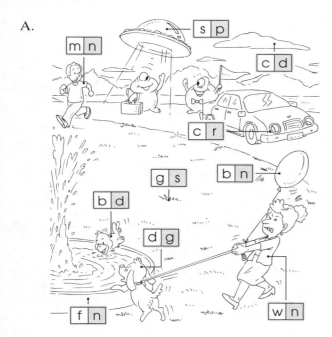

B. 1. o
   2. i
   3. u
   4. a
   5. o ; o
   6. a
   7. e
   8. u
   9. i

C. Animal: hippo ; frog
   Person: baby ; driver
   Place: beach ; park
   Thing: tomato ; plane

D.

E. one cup, three storybooks, one clock, and five pens

F. 1. ☺
   2. ☺
   3. ☺
   4. ☺
   5. ☺
   6. ☺
   7. ☺
   8. ☺

G. (In any order)
   1. What ; dot
   2. city ; pity
   3. stay ; pay
   4. here ; deer
   5. longer ; stronger
   6. there ; bear

H.　1.　? ; A
　　2.　! ; S
　　3.　? ; A
　　4.　. ; T
　　5.　? ; A
　　6.　. ; T
　　7.　! ; S
　　8.　. ; T
　　9.　! ; S

15　The Storybook Club

A.　1.　
　　2.　
　　3.　
　　4.　
　　5.　
　　6.　

B.　(Individual drawing and writing)
C.　Day of the Week:
　　Tuesday ; Sunday ; Wednesday ; Monday
　　Month of the Year:
　　May ; November ; July ; March
　　Festival:
　　Mother's Day ; Easter ; Halloween ; Thanksgiving
D.　1.　I like Christmas.
　　2.　It is on December 25.
　　3.　It is a Thursday this year.
　　4.　We are holding a party on Christmas Day.
　　5.　I will invite my friend Sandra to come.
　　6.　I will give her an invitation card this Friday.

16　Snow Day

A.　1.　✔
　　2.　✔
　　3.
　　4.　✔
　　5.
　　6.　✔
　　7.　✔
　　8.
　　9.
B.　(Individual writing and drawing)
C.　1.　?
　　2.　.
　　3.　!
　　4.　.
　　5.　?
　　6.　?
　　7.　?
　　8.　!
　　9.　.
D.　1.　Jasmine, David, and I go swimming every Sunday.
　　2.　I love having toast, sausages, and milk for breakfast.
　　3.　Pink, blue, green, and purple are my favourite colours.
　　4.　You need to bring glue, scissors, and some clips to class tomorrow.
　　5.　Put your dolls, teddy bears, and building blocks back to the toy box.
　　6.　My sister likes eating pancakes with jam, honey, or maple syrup.
　　7.　Spring, summer, fall, and winter are the four seasons in Canada.
　　8.　Do you want lollipops, chocolate, or cotton candy?

17　My Mom, the Student

A.　1.　a hospital
　　2.　healthy food
　　3.　nurse
　　4.　student
B.　1.　sick
　　2.　meals
　　3.　proud
　　4.　Maybe
　　5.　study

ISBN: 978-1-897164-29-7

C. 1. mom
   2. I
   3. pastries
   4. Dad
   5. neighbours
   6. Mrs. Wrights
   7. sons
   8. They

D. 1. girl
   2. brothers
   3. dog
   4. children
   5. boy

18 The Giant Turnip

A. 1. C
   2. B
   3. D
   4. A

B.   3 ; 5 ; 1 ; 6 ; 2 ; 4

C. 1. He
   2. They
   3. It
   4. She
   5. He
   6. It

D. 1. I
   2. I
   3. She
   4. I
   5. He
   6. He
   7. They
   8. We

19 Mr. Music's One-Man Band

A.

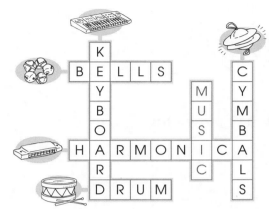

B. 1. one
   2. a drumstick
   3. on Mr. Music's ankles
   4. a harmonica

C. 1.

   2.

   3.

   4.

   5.

   6.

   7.

   8.

   9.

ISBN: 978-1-897164-29-7

D. 1. holds
2. plays
3. strikes
4. shakes
5. gives
6. claps

3. It looks like a big pot with a long handle.
4. "The Broken W" looks like a "w".

20 My New Dog

A.

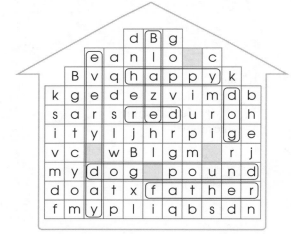

B. 1. is
2. is
3. am
4. is ; is
5. are
C. 1. are
2. are
3. is
4. am
5. is

C.

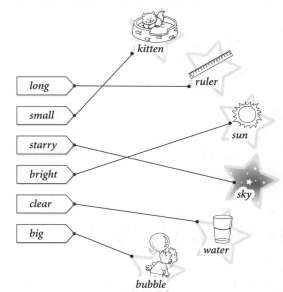

D. 1. three ;

 brown

2. one ;

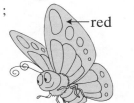 red

3. four ;

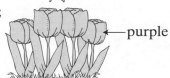 purple

4. two ;

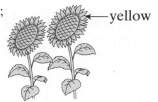 yellow

21 Starry Starry Night

A. 1. dipper
2. planet
3. astronomer
4. lopsided
5. telescope
B. 1. He is an astronomer.
2. He gave her a big telescope.

ISBN: 978-1-897164-29-7

22 Hide and Seek

A. (In any order)
2. sound ; found
3. clue ; you
4. be ; tree
5. hide ; outside
6. peek ; seek

B. 1. Hide
2. Count
3. game
4. found
5. clue

C. 1. on
2. under
3. in
4. behind
5. over

D. (Individual drawing)

23 My Wobbly Tooth

A. 1. Yesterday
2. finger
3. the Tooth Fairy
4. an apple
5. a quarter

B.

C. a: tooth ; pillow ; string ; quarter
an: apple ; oar ; onion ; elephant
the: Tooth Fairy ; sky ; world ; North Pole

D. 1. the Olympic Games
2. a dragon

3. the CN Tower
4. the Earth
5. an owl
6. an Easter egg

24 My Perfect Day

A. 1. lucky charm
2. turkey sandwich
3. singing birds
4. porridge
5. pear
6. blue dress

B. (Individual drawing and writing)

C. 1. and
2. or
3. or
4. and
5. and
6. or

D. 1. Friday or Saturday
2. Sue or Rita
3. some apples and milk
4. the puzzle or the teddy bear
5. the baseball and baseball bat

25 Riddles

A. 1. a comb
2. water

B. (Individual writing and drawing)

C. 1.
2.
3. ✔
4. ✔
5. ✔
6. ✔
7.

D. 1. The movie was long ^but we did not find it boring.
2. This dish doesn't look nice ^but it tastes good.
3. The girls play volleyball ^but the boys play soccer.

ISBN: 978-1-897164-29-7

4. The sun is shining _{but} it is also raining.

5. I want to eat a popsicle _{but} there are not any left.

E. 1. but this one is too sour
   2. but I can reach it
   3. but it is friendly
   4. but the sea water is cool

B. 1. a little scared
   2. a mouse having his teeth checked
   3. in six months
C. 1. John is hungry.
   2. It is too cold to go to the beach in winter.
   3. Those puppies are cute.
D. 1. My aunt has a candy shop.
   2. He goes fishing every weekend in summer.
   3. She will get her eighth teddy bear this summer.

26 The King of the Jungle

A. 1. fox
   2. deer
   3. tiger
   4. monkey
B. 1. The tiger tried to catch the fox.
   2. The fox said that he was the King of the Jungle.
   3. The deer were frightened and ran away.
   4. The monkeys also ran away.
   5. The tiger bowed to the fox.
   6. The fox ran proudly away.
C.   (Colour the foxes of these sentences.)
   1. The fox was in the jungle.
   2. The fox chases the rabbit.
   3. The sun is behind the clouds.
   4. The cat is eating the fish.
D. 1. Mice like eating cheese.
   2. The flowers are colourful.
   3. She puts the toys in the box.
   4. Benny is writing a letter.
   5. Who wants strawberry ice cream?
   6. The dog is hiding the candy.
   7. Where are you going?

27 My First Visit to the Dentist

A.

k	k	a	q	t	f	d	n	r	e	r	b	l	i
b	a	y	b	p	r	e	s	s	e	d	p	a	x
c	n	e	i	z	h	x	c	o	l	j	s	w	c
u	i	c	g	b	r	j	a	z	b	a	c	k	m
s	c	a	r	e	d	y	b	c	v	m	u	t	s
n	e	u	l	r	d	n	e	h	w	o	p	e	n
t	o	o	t	h	b	r	u	s	h	p	h	o	k
t	e	v	b	u	m	s	g	a	c	z	e	w	b

28 A Day with Grandpa

A.

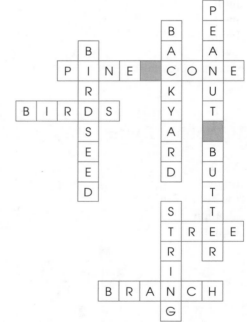

B. 1. F
   2. E
   3. D
   4. C
   5. A
   6. B
C. 1. I got the peanut butter from the fridge.
   2. I put peanut butter over a pine cone.
   3. Then my sister rolled the pine cone in birdseed.
   4. Grandpa tied a string around the pine cone.
   5. He then tied the pine cone to a branch.
   6. Soon a bird came and pecked at the pine cone.

ISBN: 978-1-897164-29-7

Review 2

A. 1. What a big kitchen!
2. We can have a big feast here at Christmas.
3. Can I invite Jim and Ross to come this Sunday?
4. Oh no! This family has a cat! /
   Oh no, this family has a cat!

B. 1. Morris ; He
2. cheese ; It
3. Gigi ; Didi ; They
4. noise ; It
5. Gigi ; She
6. You ; I ; We
7. mice ; They
8. Molly ; She

C.

D. 1. in
2. under
3. beside
4. over
5. behind

E. 1. or
2. and
3. but
4. and
5. but
6. and
7. or

F. 1. A. Kevin has a toy mouse.
   B. Kevin drinks milk every day.
   C. He likes playing with it.
   B
2. D. The toy mouse is cute.
   E. There is a key on its back.
   F. Where is the key?
   F

ISBN: 978-1-897164-29-7

1 This Is Me

A. (Individual answers)
B. (Individual drawing and answers)

2 My Life in a Timeline

(Individual answer and drawing)

3 My Family

A. (Individual photo and writing)
B. (Individual answer)
C. (Individual answers)

4 Responsibilities and Rules (1)

A. 1. D   2. A
    3. C   4. B
B. 2. No Littering
    3. Wait in Line
    4. Keep Dogs on Leash
C. (Individual writing)

5 Responsibilities and Rules (2)

A.

B. 1. B
    2. A
    3. B

6 Responsibilities, Rules, and Relationships

1. l
2. o
3. g
4. log

7 The Community

A. 1. B
    2. C
    3. A
B. 1. downtown

2. seaside

3. farm

ISBN: 978-1-897164-29-7

8 The Community Up Close

A. B ; U
   C ; S
   D ; Q
   A ; R
   E ; P

B. 1.

   2. theatre
   3. pool
   4. park
   5. (Individual writing)

9 Out and About (1)

A. 1. horse
   2. taxi
   3. bus
   4. walk
   5. car
   6. bicycle

B. 1.

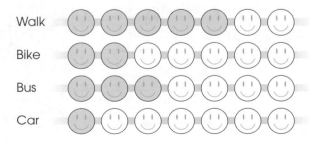

   2. walk
   3. (Individual answer)

10 Out and About (2)

A. 1. D
   2. C
   3. A
   4. B

B. 1. C
   2. A
   3. B
   4. D

C. (Individual drawing and writing)

11 Working in the Community

A. 1. E
   2. F
   3. C
   4. A
   5. D
   6. H
   7. G
   8. B

B. 1.

   2.

   3.

   4.

12 Service Workers

A. 1. D ; O
    2. A ; M
    3. E ; P
    4. F ; N
    5. C ; R
    6. B ; Q

B.

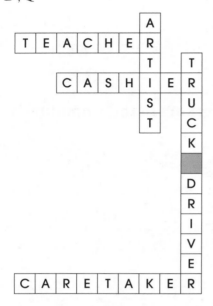

13 Safety Workers

A. 1. 1 ; 2 ; 3
    2. 3 ; 1 ; 2
B. B ; C ; D ; G
    A ; E ; F ; H

14 Health Workers

A. 1. C
    2. A
    3. B
    4. D
B. 1. C
    2. A
    3. B
    4. F
    5. D
    6. E

15 Looking at Community Workers

1. A ; M
2. E ; P
3. D ; N
4. B ; O
5. F ; R
6. C ; Q

16 Simple Maps and Directions

A. 1. a school
    2. whales
    3. two
    4. three
B. 1. left
    2. right
    3. below
    4. below ; above

17 Looking at a Grid

A.

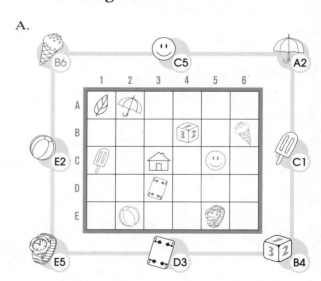

ISBN: 978-1-897164-29-7

B.

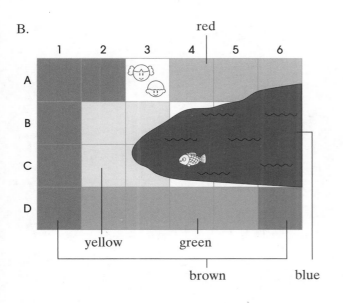

red
1 2 3 4 5 6
A
B
C
D
yellow   green
brown   blue

B.

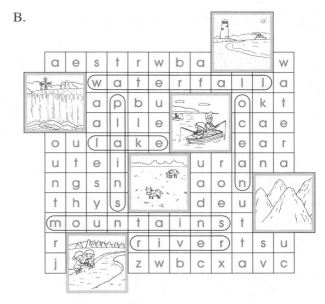

18 Streets and Distances

A. 1. 3
2. 4
3. 7
4. 9
5. 7
6. 12

B. 1. Apple Street
2. market
3. corner ; Apple Street / Care Street ;
Care Street / Apple Street
4. Apple Street / Ball Road

19 Land and Water in Canada

A. 1. lake
2. mountains
3. waterfall
4. ocean
5. river
6. plains

C. 1. ocean
2. mountain

20 Animals in Canada

A. 1. H
2. E
3. D
4. C
5. B
6. F
7. A
8. G

B.

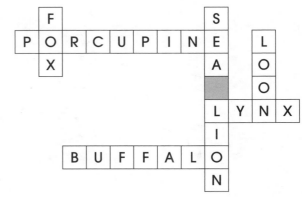

21 Knowing Our Environment

A. A ; C ; D ; H
B ; E ; F ; G
B. 1. D
2. B
3. C
4. A

22 Caring for Our Environment

A.

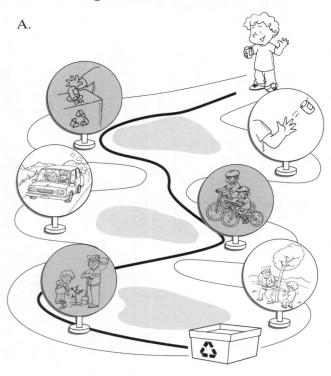

B. 1.

2.

3.

C.

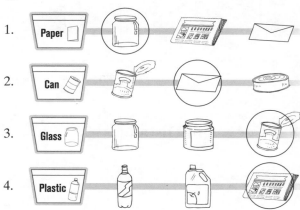

23 Smart Tools (1)

A. 1. lawn mower
2. snowblower
3. vacuum cleaner
B. 1. F
2. C
3. E
4. D
5. A
6. B

ISBN: 978-1-897164-29-7

24　Smart Tools (2)

A. 1. D
2. C
3. A
4. B
B. 1. 2 ; 1 ; 3
2. 1 ; 3 ; 2
3. 3 ; 2 ; 1

2. a. plains
b. ocean
c. mountains
d. lake
3. ocean ; natural

Review

A. (Individual answers)
B. 1. bicycle ; chef
2. bus ; farmer
3. walk ; dentist
C. 1. a. Joe
b. B2
2. a. Mary
b. B4
3. A1

D. 1.

2.

3. A
4. B
E. 1. a. C
b. E
c. G
d. F
2. below
3. left
F. 1.

1 My Body

A.
finger   head
arm   chin
back   elbow
leg   hand
foot   knee
            toe

B.

I jump with my ___ . — legs
I drum with my ___ . — hands
I play the guitar with my ___ . — fingers
I kick a ball with my ___ . — foot
I bite with my ___ . — teeth

2 Five Senses

A.
eye ; (rainbow)
ear ; (radio)
nose ; (squirrel)
tongue ; (hamburger)
skin ; (cloth)

B.
1. smell   2. nose
3. sight   4. eyes
5. touch   6. skin
7. hearing   8. ears
9. taste   10. tongue

3 Our Senses at Work

A. 1.
2.
3.
4.
5.

B. Lemon: see, touch, smell, taste
Bell: see, hear, touch
Rainbow: see

C. 1. A, B, F   2. C, D, E

4. Living Things and Their Growth

A. 1.
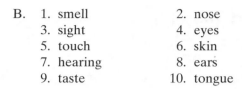

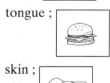

ISBN: 978-1-897164-29-7

2.

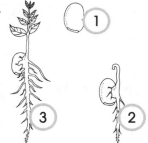

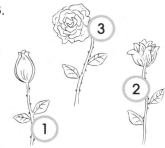

3.

4.

B.

5　Needs of Living Things

A.　1. C, D, E, I　　　2. B, F
　　 3. A, G, H
B.　1. air　　　　　　2. water
　　 3. air　　　　　　4. food
　　 5. water　　　　　6. food

6　Living Things and the Way They Move

A.　1. climb　　　　　2. hop
　　 3. swing　　　　　4. slither
　　 5. gallop　　　　　6. fly
　　 7. dive
B.　1. bouncing　　　　2. throwing
　　 3. swinging　　　　4. diving
　　 5. rolling

7　Patterns in Living Things

A.　1. ; fish

　　 2. ; tortoise

　　 3. ; leaf

　　 4. 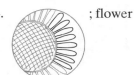 ; flower

　　 5. ; pineapple

　　 6. ; bee

B.   spots: E, G
     rings: C, D
     spiral: F, H
     stripes: A, B

8   Healthy Eating

A.   Grain Products: B, D, G, I, K, L
     Vegetables and Fruits: A, C, J, M
     Milk Products: H, N, O
     Meat and Alternatives: E, F

B.   1.   ; juice

     2.   ; popcorn

     3.   ; fresh fruit

C.

9   Safe and Healthy Living

A.

B.   1. B   2. E
     3. A   4. D
     5. C   6. F

10   Objects and Materials

A.   Colour 1, 5: blue
     Colour 2, 6: yellow
     Colour 3, 8: green
     Colour 4, 7: brown

B.   1. hard   2. heavy
     3. rough   4. dark
     5. shiny

C.   1. cement   2. glass
     3. wood

11   Materials that Join

A.   Colour the sheets with the words: mortar, thread,
     glue, nail, snap, zipper

B.   1. D   2. B
     3. E   4. F
     5. C   6. A

12   Changing Materials

A.   1.

     2.

     3.

     4.

ISBN: 978-1-897164-29-7

5.

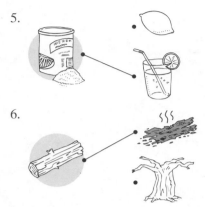

6.

B. Project 1: A ; sticky, wet
Project 2: A, D ; liquid, soft
Project 3: A, B, C, D ; thick, fluffy

13 Reuse and Recycle

A. Paper: G, H, I
Aluminum: A, D, J
Glass: B, F
Plastic: C, E, K

B.

C. (Individual drawings)

14 Energy and the Sun

A. 1. sun   2. cars
3. sailboats   4. plants
5. food   6. bodies
7. sun   8. Earth

B.

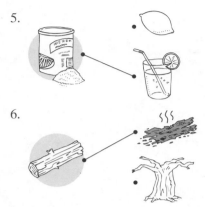

l	b	z	l	c	r	z	h
e	n	e	r	g	y	n	e
s	h	l	c	i	o	i	a
n	u	n	o	b	i	j	t
d	x	n	u	t	w	f	w
p	c	m	k	k	f	l	e
o	l	i	g	h	t	r	m

15 Energy and Food

A.

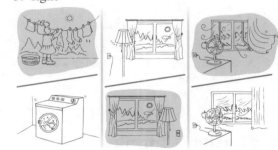

B. grass ; grasshopper ; fox ; lion
C. least to greatest: B ; D ; E ; A ; C

16 Smart Energy Use

A. 1. wood   2. oil
3. electricity   4. wind
5. sun

B. 1. hearing   2. touch
3. sight

C.

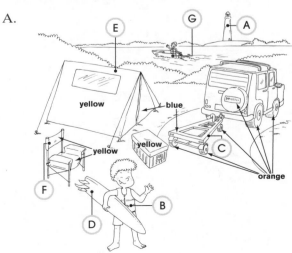

17 Structures around Us

A.

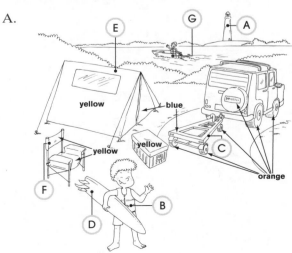

ISBN: 978-1-897164-29-7

B. 1. Colour yellow ; Rectangle
2. Colour blue ; Triangle
3. Colour orange ; Circle

C.  ; key

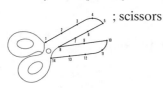 ; hanger

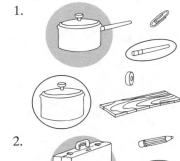 ; scissors

18 Natural Structures

A. 1. A   2. C
3. B   4. E
5. F   6. D

B. A: beaver dam   B: spider web
C: honeycomb

C. A ; D ; B ; C

19 Structures Together

A. 1.

2.

3.

4.

5.

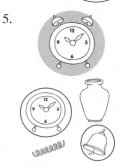

B. A, B, D, E, G, J, K, L

20 Day and Night

A. 1. It is __day__.
It is __night__.

2. It is __night__.
It is __day__.

ISBN: 978-1-897164-29-7

B. 1. A 2. B
C. A ; C ; B

21 Seasons

A. Summer: Work: B, D
Play: Q, R
Winter: Work: A, C
Play: P, S

B. 1.

C. (Individual answers)

22 Plants through the Seasons

A. 1. winter 2. spring
3. fall 4. summer
B. 1. Colour the leaf green.
2. Colour the leaf red, brown, yellow, or orange.
C. 1.

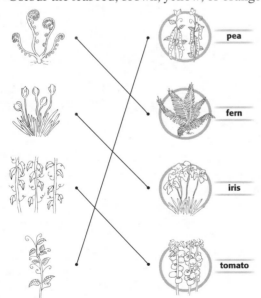

pea

fern

iris

tomato

23 Animals through the Seasons

A. 1. winter 2. fall
3. summer 4. winter
5. fall 6. spring
B. 1. B 2. C
3. A
C. winter

24 Night Animals

A.

B. 1.

2.

3.

4.

ISBN: 978-1-897164-29-7

Review

A. 1. eye ; sight
   2. nose ; smell
   3. ear ; hearing
   4. tongue ; taste
   5. skin ; touch
B. Air ; A ; F
   Water ; D ; E
   Food ; B ; C
C. 1. A, B, H, J, O   2. B, H, J, O
   3. A, E, F, O   4. G, K
   5. I, N   6. C, M
D. 1.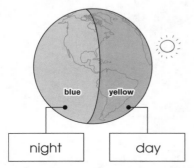
   2.
   3.
   4.
E.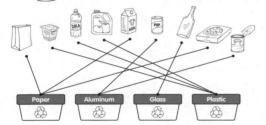
F. 1.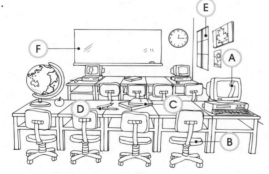
   2. (Suggested answers)
      a. blackboard   b. clock
G. 1.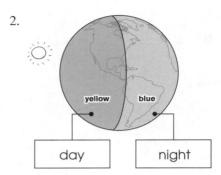
   blue   yellow
   night   day

2.
yellow   blue
day   night

H. 1. ; fall
   2.  ; spring
   3.  ; winter
   4.  ; summer

I. 1.
   2.
   3.
   4.

ISBN: 978-1-897164-29-7